CHRISTIAN Y

CHRISTIAN YOGA

by

J.-M. DÉCHANET, O.S.B.

TUNBRIDGE WELLS

SEARCH PRESS

SEARCH PRESS LIMITED
Wellwood, North Farm Road, Tunbridge Wells, Kent

First published April 1960
Eighth impression 1984

This translation of La Voie du Silence, *3rd edition (Desclée de Brouwer, Paris)*
and additions by the author, was made by
ROLAND HINDMARSH

MADE AND PRINTED IN GREAT BRITAIN BY
BIDDLES LTD, GUILDFORD AND KING'S LYNN FOR
SEARCH PRESS LTD.

CONTENTS

PREFACE

SINCE the publication of the second French edition of this book, I have often been asked how I came to be mixed up in this sort of thing; by what tricks of destiny or chance conflux of circumstance a discipline taken from the East had succeeded in foisting itself on my thought, which—as my previous writing showed—had been entirely nourished in the Western tradition.

The answer is quite simple. However strange it may appear, I was led to Yoga by William of Saint-Thierry. For twenty years I lived under the aegis and influence of his living psychology, which in turn had been taken and adapted from Origen (himself an Oriental), and my greatest concern has been to ensure that in me there should exist that balance of *anima*, *animus* and *spiritus* which he makes the precondition —a point he stresses over and over again in all sorts of ways in his writing—of the unfolding in man of the grace of our Lord, and of the transition from the image (the mark of which is clearly set on these "three") to divine resemblance. The creature, cut off from God by sin and divided, moreover, within himself, cannot entertain the hope of finding his creator or his lost intimacy with him otherwise than by first of all making use of the grace of Christ the redeemer and of his power and example, in order to fashion himself anew in the image of God, to re-establish unity in himself, and to rediscover the natural order in the order of charity. With the spirit cleaving to God (in love and through love) intelligence and the thinking soul must follow the motions of the spirit;

and finally the body, itself bearing the mark of grace, must obey thought and make the interests of the spirit wholly its own. In this way nature, turned aside from God by original sin, will rediscover the fundamental unity and harmony that belonged to it before the Fall; and man, the whole of man, will once more be able to shape a course towards God.

During the last few years I spent long hours pondering over these ideas of William of Saint-Thierry. To live entirely for God, to move towards him, with my "three" properly in balance, with my body playing its part, and my soul with all its lofty considerations withdrawing when required, so that the voice of the Almighty might be heard in my heart— this had become a kind of obsession with me. The question was, how to attain this condition.

I had been an invalid from childhood on; but when I was about forty, I was providentially cured, and felt a consuming urge to live. I worked with my head; I worked with my hands. Yet this overflowing activity partially obstructed my life of prayer and my hunger for contemplation. I was not growing, not developing—or too little, at any rate, for my liking. Something in me was and stayed dead.

I took up sports. I was forty-two before I learnt to swim. I did gymnastics with young people. I took part in a course where I quickly benefited from a system that aimed at making a man "a new being, well balanced in body as well in mind and full of energy". I found the training very hard, but I took the whole system as an ascetic discipline; for I wanted to have, not merely strong muscles, but strength of soul, a virile temperament and above all an openness of spirit, reaching up and out towards higher things. After six months I noticed a definite improvement at all levels of being and action. I had greater resistance, I was less susceptible to fatigue, I could do more and do it better; and in addition I experienced a characteristic phenomenon—after my morning session of "physical culture", I felt the need to make my way to the church.

During this period I happened to see an article in a magazine, extolling the beneficial effects of certain Yoga postures. I sensed at once that this gymnastics of repose, more suited to my age as well as to my way of life than the exercises I had been doing, would carry me further at the spiritual level. I felt that, as it was centred more on interior activity, it should make my body a fitter instrument for contemplation and for the contemplative life, and above all that it would effect this union or joining together of my "three" (*anima—animus—spiritus*) of which I still was dreaming.

What I then read about Yoga and about some of its aims simply encouraged me to embark on, and then go through with, an experiment about the appropriateness of which I became convinced at the very first attempt. Yoga, I found, was first of all "a particular way of fashioning oneself", the way of the man who "by means of certain disciplines, both physiological [postures and breath-control] and psychical [focusing of thought], was joined; that is to say, was in a condition of coherence in accordance with his vital functions, and in a state of balance such that life could be controlled and made effective. This is therefore the opposite of fragmented living, of naïve incoherence, impotence and unawareness". Its symbol is "the wheel, where the rim is perfectly jointed to the nave by means of the spokes."[1] But Yoga was also joining with the Absolute. And here I had to be careful. It was essential that my exercises and especially my concentration should turn me not towards the Self, the It, the Absolute, the Wholly-One, the vague

[1] Cf. P. Masson-Oursel, "Yoga: what it is not, what it is, and what it can become", in *Yoga, science de l'homme intégral*, Cahiers du Sud, Paris, 1953, pp. 6 and 7. A similar definition is to be found in a study by M. Olivier Lacombe, "Sur le Yoga indien", in *Études Carmélitaines*, 22nd year, 1937, p. 167.

"Ungraspable" of Hindu mystics, but towards the God of Abraham, Isaac and Jacob, the living God, three in one, the principle of all things, my Creator and Father, him in whom I had natural and supernatural life. I felt it was absolutely necessary that my experiment should place itself under the protection and sanction of grace. Not heaven-storming; but, instead, working to remove certain blockages within that were hindering supernatural action. Not to turn in on myself; but on the contrary to launch myself outwards towards the Other, to lose myself in him, to fix my thinking and especially my heart in God, in the God of love, and in Christ; and to maintain the sort of silence that would be a form of mute speech or dialogue with the Eternal.

Every day, then, I carried out my exercises; I also read a lot about Yoga. Those who have blamed me for having, as it were, "scratched the surface" of this complicated system without getting at its heart do not seem to have any idea of the labour of "conversion" that I deliberately undertook—to disengage a number of practices from their matrix and then to introduce them into Christian living so as to form a Christianity both integrated and whole.[2]

After I had recited Matins and said Mass, I shut myself in my room for an hour, and, whatever the temperature, I carried out by the open window a series of exercises neither more nor less peculiar than those in "normal" physical culture, and familiar to many people. I have already described these exercises and given an account of their initial effects,

[2] My "scratching" was in fact pretty thorough. By setting aside the "accidents" of the method, I tried to grasp its soul and substance, first through books, essays and interpretations that were sometimes mutually contradictory (on this point see a criticism of Olivier Lacombe, *op. cit.*, by Swāmi Siddheswarānanda, in *Études sur Ramana Maharshi*, Adyar, Paris, 1949, pp. 171–2); and then through my own experience. This experience is worth what it is worth. And even though it may, or inevitably must, throw some light on the problem of Christian Yoga, that is nevertheless not its aim at all.

which perhaps shared the same nature with those I had experienced from the previous system, but certainly differed in type. To this point I shall return. What was really new about them, when compared with my previous experiment, was the extraordinary sense of calm in me after each session, and at the same time the ease I felt in entering into prayer, in concentrating on a subject, or on a particular point, in the manner I called "silent meditation". I took the habit of linking the latter to the postures and breathing exercises of Yoga. I "caught on" straightway, mostly to Christ as he appeared in the Gospel for the day. Some word fallen from his lips, or a gesture made by his "holy and worshipful" hands held my attention; or else some aspect of his person and his message. I shall never forget the sober intoxication, the calm happiness that took possession of my soul one day in Advent 19.., when I opened myself to the idea: "There is one who enlightens every soul born into the world; he was the true Light."

For ten minutes, fifteen, more even, I remained in this state, completely still in mind and body. After six months of painful efforts, the Perfect posture had become natural. I often chose to hold the posture for longer. If anyone had come upon me by surprise, sitting on my mat, he would no doubt have thought me mad. But I was carrying out to the letter the advice in the Gospel: "Shut yourself in to pray." I was never once disturbed.

This was the time of day when, only a short while before, I had been in the habit of working at my books and articles. Composition had normally come easily during this period of the morning, when my mind was at its most lucid and I was least taken up with monastic duties. But now it is to silence that I devote this time, to a silence filled with God and with prayer; and I can only be forced to omit or shorten it here and there by the pressure of certain duties and the demands of

Chapter. Moreover, from this fidelity to prayer—so easy to keep up—my work does not suffer; I have in fact never written so much. . . .

By becoming clearly contemplative in a matter of weeks, my prayer had been given a particular and novel cast; and this was matched by the distinctness in the repercussions my daily sessions of exercises were having on my everyday life, as well as on the many different occupations which a monk is vowed to carry out. The genuine sense of euphoria that followed the exercises persisted in me and transfigured my day. During the early months I had to face up to the sort of difficulties which put one's nerves to the test, and which would certainly have put me on my back before. As it was, everything went off so smoothly, and I took it all so well, that I trained everyone under my charge to develop the attitude of "accepting rather than undergoing".

On the physical plane, the problems of general health disappeared; I no longer suffered from those fits of tiredness and temperature that pointed clearly to overwork. I found myself possessed of an extremely supple body ready to serve me and pleased at no longer being a hindrance to the life of the spirit. Fasting had formerly been very difficult for me. Today I feel an imperative need not to take more than a minimum of food at breakfast. Similarly with other restraints. The one form of ascetic discipline, passive in a sense, runs parallel with the other and places me well clear of any kind of misconstrued asceticism, and even further from any commonplace "voluntarism". Fasting, it is true, remains a mortification; but it is in addition, and to a greater extent, a symbol.

It is a symbol of detachment—of a certain measure of detachment—from events and things; a sign of peace, of the establishment of calm, in short, of liberation at the very heart of the human complex that is me. True, the inevitably complicated problems of my nature have not disappeared. But they no longer occur in that sharp, dramatic, obsessive character that until recently they sometimes assumed. I feel free, very much freer, with regard to certain attractions; I have shaken off something that tended to complicate my private life, my life as a man.

People have written to me to say that my "method" had proved of great assistance in some instances of sexual psychosis. I am not surprised, for Yoga immediately struck me as a stabilizing factor in this sphere.

I am simply stating the fact. It strikes me as richly symbolic. I am sure that this method—for that is what it consists of—will serve mankind, young, adolescent, and married, not only because it makes it easier for everyone to practise chastity, but also and perhaps mainly because it removes the frequently morbid character of sexual desire or attraction.[3] The exercises of Yoga clarify the relationship between body and soul, and soul and body. They establish a kind of agreement; and from this interpenetration the spirit, the heart, only stands to gain.

The excellent effect the exercises have on people suffering from other complexes should also be mentioned; on the timid, the inhibited, the tough, the violent, the proud. Here I only wish to mention how these people brought me to realize how very deeply they stood in need of kindness, gentleness and compassion from me. I used to like scoring a point off others, without malicious intent, but in the end. . . . Again, I used to be inclined to controversy; now I am more pacific, having been set at peace myself.

Above all I feel I am more faithful to my calling as a

[3] The very rare exceptions to this that have been reported to me go to prove the rule.

Christian, and to my ideal as a monk. The fact is there; how can it be explained? Since deciding to become a yogi—a "yogi of Christ" was what I wrote⁴—I discovered within my reach a whole programme which until then had seemed to me, if not distant, at least neither close, nor easily accessible. I am not going to talk drivel and assert that even then I did not know about the Beatitudes, about various pieces of advice given by our Lord—in a word, the Gospel in letter and in spirit. There are in fact plenty of ways of "knowing" something, of being in possession of a doctrine, or of being informed regarding a message—even the message of the Gospel. Apart from and transcending the "ordinary" way of knowing, there is in particular the kind of understanding of the man who "reads within himself" (*intus-legit*), with his heart properly disposed (*in affectu cordis*, as William of Saint-Thierry puts it), the truth that concerns him, that very matter that he must come to know or get done. This is for me (so runs the attitude of such a man), there is a correspondence between me and this ideal, aim, programme; I can feel it, we are made for each other. From this kind of knowing or understanding, from this contemplation—as it should rightly be called—to action there is but one step. Or rather, as soon as he knows, understands, contemplates in this way, he is vitally attached to the object. This *engagement* proceeds from love. In this way, then, my life gradually opened out on vistas of whose existence I had admittedly not been completely ignorant (I rather think the opposite), but which I had always regarded from a distance, as things known from afar and held in fitting respect. It is thus that I came to understand (to *stand under*) certain pages of the Gospel.

⁴ I signed the first French edition of this book "Yogi of Christ"; by this I meant "that I intended to do Yoga so as to help myself to be *of* Christ". If I had simply written: "A Christian yogi", the expression would not have looked so odd, but it would not have emphasized the essential point in my aim.

Thanks to Yoga, without any doubt. I know well enough that the exercises in this ancient discipline furthered the discovery and especially the establishment in man of clearly defined tendencies: non-violence, truthfulness, chastity, poverty. But I did not know—at least, not as a fact, though I felt it instinctively—that carrying out these exercises would at the same time produce in me a real need of living the Sermon on the Mount, of understanding and of grasping, otherwise than by thought, the true dimensions of the Christian Beatitudes, both on the level of world history and on that of inner life.

This I have now realized. God forbid that I should boast of being poor, gentle and meek. But I am striving to attain these virtues. Every day the exercises, and indeed the whole ascetic discipline of my Yoga, make it easier for the grace of Christ to flow in me. I feel my hunger for God growing, and my thirst for righteousness, and my desire to be a Christian in the full strength of the word—to be for Christ, to be of Christ, without any half-measures or reservations.

It remains for me to make one point clear, so as to prevent any misconceptions. In writing *Christian Yoga* I obviously did not intend to solve the important problem which today is busying a number of people very well informed about Indian forms of Yoga, and who are, moreover, eager to see the Christian West "work out a Yoga of its own". My very modest aim was primarily practical.[5] My friend, Father

[5] The first French edition of this book (*La Voie du Silence*), which was submitted to some specialists for comment, bore the sub-title "A method of contemplation based on Yoga". Although it was full of Sanskrit terminology, it already represented—as the title implies—a complete transposition. This is what a friend, now a hermit in India, wrote to me after reading it: "You have gone a lot further than I have. You have come to Yoga with the innocence of the dove and the wariness of the serpent. With innocence, in that you have taken the instrument as you found it and have used it to good effect in your

Régamey, has been kind enough to stress this.[6] Nevertheless, the pseudonym "Yogi of Christ" (the meaning of which has already been explained), together with certain chapters and numerous details, have not failed to estrange some "Indianizers", Catholic and non-Catholic. Without giving the impression of having touched on the question, I have in fact none the less taken my stand. It is only right that I should state my position more clearly.

In this book I have to some extent restricted myself to examining the easiest and most accessible form of Yoga, Hatha Yoga. A start must be made somewhere. It is stupid to aim too high; you have to learn to walk before you can run. The harvest only ripens after having gone through certain changes; or, to change the metaphor, the results are only achieved at the end of a patient apprenticeship. The Indian is conditioned for Yoga by his milieu, by the whole matrix of his upbringing; but he does not throw himself into the mysteries of Rāja Yoga—the Royal Yoga—or of Jñāna Yoga —the Yoga of Knowing—until he has gained mastery over his body, unified his vital forces, and thoroughly stabilized all the forms of energy in him (this last is the main aim of Hatha Yoga). *A fortiori*, the European or Westerner, before hoping to "enter immediately on the path of the mystical

praying; with wariness, in that you have not turned down the darker pathways towards control of the subconscious where Indian Yoga normally leads. You have been brought, as if by a short cut, to reap its benefits, yet your experience has been Christian through and through. The way you practise the āsanas [postures] is entirely free from suspicion. As you point out, it takes its roots in a very sane view of man that is completely in harmony with our doctrine of the Incarnation. The benefits you have reaped have all the wholesomeness of a simple, sincere, straightforward prayer, reaching to the living God in his profoundest mystery, that of the Most Holy Trinity." Later on when acknowledging the receipt of my book, this hermit friend remarked on the increased assimilation shown in the new edition as well as the higher degree of personal colouring.

[6] Cf. *La Vie spirituelle*, November 1956, pp. 439–42.

life" as so many yogis do, must work towards removing various hindrances, and become familiar with an ascetic discipline the meaning of which in many cases has become lost to him. To get rid of a few problems in general health, to increase one's capacity for work, to make one's character gentler and stronger, to free oneself of various complexes, to create in oneself a whole atmosphere of calm and silence, and to do this by exercises in a gymnastic of repose and by a simple but careful method of breath-control—such aims may appear humble enough, rather down to earth, and a far cry from the goal of even the most modest of yogis. Yet I am certain that they will be able to work real miracles here in the West; to change lives and temperaments completely, making them healthier, more open; to increase their degree of *engagement*; and to render them more receptive to impulses and promptings from heaven.

I do not intend here to betray the cause of Yoga—of the Christian Yoga that people are dreaming of—by stating that the problem that it puts to us all must *first of all* be put squarely at the level of human life and of mental balance. It is certainly not a mere matter of hygiene and equanimity. But it should be pointed out to those among us whose eyes are turned to the East, as well as made clear to the specialist themselves (who too frequently are prisoners of theory and strangers to practice), that the very first service the Westerner must ask of Yoga is to teach him to become, to re-become, a man—a fully human being, human in the complete sense, in the light of Faith and of Revelation.

Neither angel nor beast, man is a being who but seldom accepts to be what he is, and who does not always understand that he must aim at growth and expansion both in his nature and in the life of grace. In his nature (as made by God), at all stages of his physical, intellectual and moral life; in grace, since nature is in fact taken under the charge of grace, since no one may boast that he is able to make his way relying solely on his own powers.

Man must accept himself for what he is. At certain periods of history it was the done thing in some circles to pare away various manifestations of the instincts and of the noblest forms of energy in man, under the pretext of their harming spiritual life. Things were cut back to the minimum, and "animal" life and genuinely intellectual aspirations were in fact suppressed. It was neither thought nor believed that the solution to the conflict already spoken of by St Paul could be found in synthesis and, to put it briefly, in the expansion of and development of man's activities in a hierarchy or order— the order of nature itself, upraised by the order of grace or of charity.

Nowadays, to be sure, we are more "comprehensive". In particular, we pay more attention to the body. It may even be that we go too far. On the other hand, are there not too many intellectuals about who, without knowing it, have put a muzzle on their hearts, and whose "spiritual life" misses those deep intuitions that are of the world of the spirit?

All these people—the "brains", the spiritualists, as well as those who are embarrassed or engrossed by the body—may be taught by Yoga (I say "may", because they have to give themselves to it) that they cannot become truly themselves unless they accept their nature as men and aim at establishing balance between the parts of man in us; this nature of ours which is at one and the same time an animal body (*corpus-anima*), thinking soul (*animus-mens*) and spirit (*spiritus-cor*). It is a harmony among these "three" that is sought in each of us by the grace of redemption. Christ came in the first place so that this "creature of God" within us, concealed under a human complex, bruised and torn by original sin, should flower and open out in its full beauty and wealth of talent.

Any ascetic discipline that works towards this works, in fact, hand in hand with grace, and that is why I have roundly stated that a Yoga that calms the senses, pacifies the soul, and frees certain intuitive or affective powers in us can be of inestimable service to the West. It can make people into true Christians, dynamic and open, by helping them to be men.

To do this, however, this Yoga must show a humility and modesty of aim. It must also take into account our own riches and our heritage. When somebody points me out those yogis in the Himalayas, or Benares, or Travancore, those prodigies of energy who rely heavily on psycho-physiological techniques to bring about "major changes in the courses of their inner lives",[7] and thereby become united with the "divine principle at work in the universe" in their isolation and their enstasy, I cannot help remarking that what they are seeking with such effort is here with us, right by us: the Creator in his Word, God supreme in his love.

We in the West are too easily impressed by the "high claims" made for Hindu Yoga (such as the power to change the course of development of the inner life), by the performances of its devotees, both orthodox and heterodox, and even by the goals aimed at by certain swāmis.[8] We are then in danger of forgetting and completely losing sight of the first, essential aim of this discipline of Yoga, with its hundred different looks and manifold incarnations—the joining,

[7] Cf. M. R. Amadou, "Yoga Chrétien?" in *Combat*, Sept. 13th, 1956: "Yoga claims that it directly affects the unfolding of the mystical life by its very psycho-physiological techniques." On this subject see O. Lacombe, "Un exemple de mystique naturelle, l'Inde", in *Études carmélitaines*, 23rd year, 1938; pp. 140–51; and J. Maritain, "L'expérience mystique naturelle et le vide", *ibid.*, pp. 116–39.

[8] This was appropriately pointed out again during a recent discussion in which there arose the question of parapsychological states in Yoga. Cf. *La Tour saint-Jacques*, No. 6–7, Paris, 1956, p. 163: the remarks made by Emilio Servadio during the conference presided over by J. Bruno, on *Yoga et Parapsychologie expérimentale*.

already mentioned, of the elements that make man so as to effect the union of man with the origin of his being. If that in fact is the goal of Yoga, then yogic practice is clearly a function of the particular idea that the devotee forms on the one hand of man and of various elements in man, and on the other, of God himself. The projections that arise from it and the forms of development it takes are in keeping with a particular faith and with a philosophy and a doctrine of man related to this faith. In Brahmanic, Buddhistic, Sufi and similar circles, which are without revelation and forced to work out a philosophical system without stable and positive data, that is to say in those circles where man is a prisoner of his psyche, of his "self", with neither the prospect nor the hope nor the possibility of soaring up towards Another, towards a living God, it is normal for the struggle for union and unity to come to an end once and for all in the disruption of the normal interplay of his powers, in the disintegration of *anima* and *animus* in favour of *spiritus*, and in producing states that profoundly modify the course of the inner life. He is necessarily driven into a *via negativa*, by the absolute or quasi-absolute absence of any positive datum about nature or even about existence of a God, the object of contemplation, knowledge and love. Moreover, he considers himself as a part of the divine Absolute, but a part enveloped in darkness, submerged in an ocean of sordid illusions, a prisoner within the shell of his thinking and acting self. The Indian devotee of Yoga is therefore reduced to asking ecstasy to give him a particular form of itself, a form that is conditioned and called out by subjective states. This form is called samadhi,[9] the piercing realization of the true "Self", the identification of

[9] This is really not a matter of ecstasy (standing outside oneself), but of enstasy, the extreme form of concentration on oneself, a complete turning inwards. Cf. Mircea Eliade, "Chamanisme et techniques yogiques indiennes", in *Yoga, loc. cit.*, pp. 113-15.

Self with Brahman, the Impersonal Infinite from which all things arise.

How differently things stand with a Christian who clings to the content of his *Credo*. Before him he has the Eternal, the living God, Father, Son and Holy Ghost. This God presents himself to him as an object worthy of attainment, true, but also as an ocean, a bottomless chasm in which the Christian must lose himself, must melt, at the end of a road whose stages are marked for him not by a *guru*, however wise and experienced he might be, but by the sovereign master, Christ, Word of God, God himself, the Way, the Truth and the Life. He knows he must make his way under the sign of redemption, in the order of charity, not alone but with the Other, with and in his grace. The idea of expecting techniques, however pure and lofty, to unite him with the Absolute cannot occur to him. "That love resides, not in our shewing any love for God, but in his shewing love for us first" (I John 4.10). Hence the very first act of a Christian believing in love is to open himself to receive him who comes down to him. With the Christian, every technique is subordinated to the initiative coming from God. The silent monologue of the Hindu ascetic on his mat contrasts with the no less silent dialogue (for it is not made up by words) of every Christian from the humblest to the most mystical, each anxious to respond to the approaches and attentions of his God.

Any Yoga that is to be Christian must respect and serve this fundamental trait in Christianity. While it is possible to adapt Hatha Yoga to fit this basic requirement without very much trouble, the same is not true of other forms of Yoga. Rāja Yoga, for instance, seems to be in essence, an absolute turning inwards on oneself; a condition where one has cut oneself off from everything, including all positive and objective knowledge. Rāja Yoga is the night of the senses and of the mind, but not, as in traditional Christian mysticism, in the meaning of a predominantly *passive* purification of our human faculties, which, already in possession of the truth, are being made more receptive to supernatural light by divine action. On the contrary, in Rāja Yoga there is active plucking away and casting aside of the things of matter, of sense and particularly of intellect; it is "an effort to withdraw oneself from māyā, the great cosmic illusion,"[10] an absolute silence of the mind that shuts itself off from any outside influence, even though this should be divine. It is a direct realization of the "self"; a mysticism lacking both dogma and faith. It is obvious to anyone that a tendency of this kind is incompatible with the essence of Christianity and in contradiction with the experience of the saints.

But the objection will perhaps be raised that even though the spirit of Rāja Yoga may not be susceptible of adaptation, it may be possible to make use of its disciplines. The main features of these are well known: strict breath-control, maintained for hours; mastery of the circulation of the blood; intense and protracted concentration; "visualization" of the object by the subject at a given point of the body, up to the point of identifying himself with it.[11] These are dangerous disciplines, and must be treated with greatest circumspection. I do not, however, deny that it is possible to keep some of all this, in particular for the practice of prayer and meditation. I

[10] Fr Bruno de Jésus-Marie pointed this out already over twenty years ago in "Mystique hindoue, mystique chrétienne", in *Études Carmélitaines*, 1932, p. 159: "From the Christian viewpoint it seems inconceivable to attempt a valid comparison between the supernatural nights of the senses and of the mind (as in St John of the Cross) and the realizations of the 'Self'." I should add that, in my humble opinion, and notwithstanding certain remarks that have been made to me, it appears no more conceivable to put side by side the *via negativa* of a Hindu jñāni with that of the Greek Fathers or of Meister Eckhart. The latter is a late stage in a process whose origin lies in the obscure but positive way of faith. It denies only so as to assert more strongly.

[11] The sun, for example, is visualized at the different plexuses of the body; and the subject identifies himself with it.

know very well how much can be derived from ten minutes in the Pole posture, followed by another ten in the Full Backwards Bend or Reintegration posture, when breathing has become so slow and deep that it may seem as if the breath reaches the base of the intestines or the perineum. Then there is no difficulty in attaching yourself wholly to the subject of prayer. I say "wholly", for you feel truly "re-collected", gathered together; you are fully in possession and control of yourself, and each time you have the distinct impression of never having given yourself to God so completely and above all so truly. The body is still, perfectly relaxed, thanks to the Lotus posture; you are not bothered by it any more—in fact you forget it! The activity of the various vital currents really enters into play in prayer. An extraordinary sense of calm sinks into the mind, while from the depths of the soul there rises up towards God a silent concert, as it were, of praise and adoration. It is not necessarily—in fact I don't believe it is at all—"the intermission of any definite thought", but rather the fixation of intuitive (not discursive) thinking on an idea or an object. It is less a concentration of intellectual faculties than a projection of the whole being towards Another. Nor is it a turning in of the spirit on itself—though in fact the spirit does become aware of what it is and has—but a silence in the spirit in which without saying anything, even to oneself, many things may be grasped and understood.

That, then, is admittedly a cautious, but at any rate a sensible application of the disciplines of Rāja Yoga to prayer. It can certainly be taken further, but it is for the Christian yogis-to-be to teach us how far we may venture on this tricky, dangerous terrain. The essential point is to understand thoroughly and to admit *that it is not a question of turning a given form of Yoga into something Christian,* but of bringing onto the service of Christianity and of the Christian life (especially when this is given up to contemplation) the undoubted benefits arising from yogic disciplines. Everything in Yoga, therefore, that promotes dialogue, the basic Christian dialogue, may be boldly considered as fit for adaptation. On the other hand, whatever makes for involution and isolation must be banished. Any over-valuation of material techniques for the mystical quest for God is suspect; likewise any over-estimation of a form of "spiritualism" which would tend to resuscitate—though only in the letter—the Platonic dualism of certain Church Fathers. Christianity is founded on an incarnation, that of the Son of God; and it is that that must give the characteristic look and authentic worth to the Christian Yoga dreamt of. It matters little then if the *gurus* of the East are chary of giving this Yoga their recognition.

INTRODUCTION

WE do not have to look about us very far or for very long to realize the disastrous effects produced on the inner life of man by this age of noise. Spun about in the whirl of business, enslaved to countless technical inventions, man is severed from God and from the world of the spirit. *Non in commotione Deus*: God does not dwell in turbulence. To find him, there must be calm within; certain senses must be hushed. Tossed around as we are, if God wishes to speak to us, his voice, small and still, will be lost in the hubbub of our daily lives; the rackets and noise drowning our minds will prevent his penetration into that seclusion we call "heart"— the living witness of that life in us which is most sacred and most true: the life we call "inner" or "spiritual".

Go into any church on a Sunday while Mass is being said. Amongst those that are there "fulfilling their obligations", how many are really following what is happening at the altar? How many have in fact come to pray, to recollect themselves, to draw peace of mind, content of soul, and the unfolding of their true being from contact with God? And above all, how many of those who have come into the church to pray have prepared themselves for prayer by forgetting their work and worries for a moment, by breaking free from the harsh clutch of life's needs? Very few, we may be sure. However good a man's intentions may be, he is fettered by the material side of life, and in the maelstrom of worldly affairs he is snatched far away from God and from the things of the spirit. Hundreds of millions of human beings cannot manage to rise beyond the mere struggle for existence; they live out their lives, little concerned with mind or even soul, and die, not ennobled in stature, but shrunken. And those that want to burst through the confines of their own selves, to get beyond their worries and preoccupations, are most often jolted to a standstill by such difficulties that, not seldom, they give up. A whole world is noisy within them, a world more difficult to avoid than the external racket, from which one can still find shelter. For there exist even nowadays oases of silence: a church, a monastery, or, failing these, a forest, a quiet room. They will be standing ready to admit whoever needs peace and calm in which to reflect and restore himself. Yet being alone and withdrawn may not enable every man to shake off what is weighing him down or holding him back. He may not be able to sweep out all his own rubbish, or to control his feelings and emotions; he may not be able to pull aside that screen of human thoughts and domestic cares and daily moiling about that almost automatically sets itself up in front of the mind as soon as it wishes to turn to God, and, letting everything that is happening round about slip away, rise towards eternal things. "God, the rest is silence", wrote a French thinker. Yet how difficult this very withdrawing from the racket of the mind is, so that only the murmuring of the voice of the living God is heard, soft and light as an exhalation—*sibilus aurae tenuis* (I Kings 19.12).

To return to the subject of monasteries: Let us admit right away that the noise of the world gets in there without any difficulty. In itself, this point is negligible, but what does matter is that "the meaning of silence has been lost by the very men who make it their profession—the monks". This remark is not mine, but Father Régamey's, who, however, does not develop the matter any further. "This fundamental topic," he writes, "demands a whole chapter to itself. There is indeed a lot to be written, many words, about silence."[1] In his stead we may say *inter alia* that wherever you go there are monks to be found who experience difficulty in

[1] "La sagesse du corps" in *Vie spirituelle*, Nov. 1955, p. 364.

restoring themselves through mental prayer, which was held in such great esteem by their predecessors. Liturgical prayer—the great prayer of the monasteries—is shorn more and more of those moments of heart-to-heart intimacy with God that used to mark it, as well as of those practices which St Benedict recommends in his Rule in the chapter "Of the Oratory of the Monastery": "When the Work of God is finished, let all go out in deep silence, and let reverence for God be observed, so that any brother who may wish (*forte*) to pray privately be not hindered by another's misbehaviour. And at other times also, if anyone wish (*forte*) to pray secretly, let him just go in and pray: not in a loud voice, but with tears and fervour of heart."[2]

Granted, we still see monks in prayer in the churches and chapels of our monasteries. But we have to admit that the two *forte*'s with which St Benedict points his text apply more today than they did in the sixth century.

This does not imply a general loss of esteem for "private" prayer so much as "drought in the soul" and "inhibited feeling", exacerbated by a kind of "habitual nervous agitation"[3] kept going by the need to move, to speak, to do something, and by a sense of powerlessness to get oneself away from the world of noise.

We are now scarcely able to imagine "public" prayer being interrupted today, as it used to be, by pauses and moments of silence between the psalms. These breaks for meditation, which St Benedict already wished to have short,[4] were replaced long ago by antiphons, on which we hardly for a moment think of fixing our thoughts, much less our hearts.

---

[2] *Rule of St Benedict*, Ch. 52, translated and edited by Abbot Justin McCann, Burns Oates, London, 1952.
[3] Cf. Régamey, *art. cit.*, p. 372.
[4] Cf. *Rule.*, Ch. 20.

Can we think of a High Mass nowadays without organ accompaniment? Let us leave aside the rowdy entries and exits of Pontifical Mass. During the sacrifice itself, the consecration bell only just manages to bring down a minute or two of silence on the sanctuary. That we are inured to this surely proves that the meaning of silence is atrophied in us. *Taciturnitas* is no longer for us the second nature that it was for our fathers. We are always having trouble in keeping silence and recollecting ourselves. Someone once told me that one religious superior found it inconvenient—*odiose*—for the silent prayer following the liturgical *flectamus genua* to last for longer than an Our Father; the same prayer has recently been reinstated in certain offices by the Congregation of Rites. This anecdote provides a telling instance, not of the falling esteem in which silent prayer is held, but of the difficulty met with in giving oneself up to it, even in the cloister, and above all in that sudden manner, on the mere invitation of a priest or deacon during Office. We cannot do it; we do not know how to.

All of us, both religious and lay, are probably suffering from a deeper disease, which may be striking at, I shall not say something essential in Christianity, but nevertheless at something vital and important.

The *spiritual life* of Christians has never been in danger of confusion with their *experience of God*. Nor would it seem, on the other hand, that some experience of God and of the things of God has ever been wanting in a genuinely spiritual life. Now it may be asked whether nowadays there does not exist in the mind a kind of depreciation of religious experience, and of the mystical life, even in its commonest form. God appears to have withdrawn far off. Has he withdrawn from men; or do men, for the reasons set out above, lend themselves less to his approaches and visits? With a lot of people, firm and zealous Christians carefully carrying out their duties, the life of faith is supported less than it used to be by personal contact with their Father who is in heaven. Very often, though not always, Christian experience is left unbuttressed by the intimacy with Jesus Christ which can be observed in the early Church (see the Apocalypse). Charity is frequently reduced to its essentially active aspect: devotion to God, and even more to one's neighbour. Few men are really aware of the indwelling of God, and of the Spirit in their hearts. We are told: "Whoever wishes to have in him this presence of the Most High, let him not experiment." True enough. But how many are making themselves fit to receive this boon? How many are even thinking of doing so? And how many, for that matter, are able to?

We are brought back to this hindrance: the deadweight on the spirit that prevents a man from entering into a deeper life, and the difficulty he has in finding the inner calm he needs in order to speak with God.

In the East there exists a large group of thoroughly tested techniques that could be termed the way or path of silence. From distant times, sages in India have been teaching men to keep mastery over their thoughts, to control their psychic being, and to establish themselves in an atmosphere of relaxation and profound peace, far from everything "noising" in man and around him; and all this has been achieved by means of a series of physical disciplines. Might we, of the West, not be able to profit from this authentic experience of theirs, and, while keeping in mind the differences in temperament, culture and especially faith, might we not make use of their methods to find again the way to God—to a God from whom our civilization and technology, our habits and all the noise surrounding our daily routines have already cut us off, and threaten to divorce us irrevocably? Should we not be able, at their school, to reawaken our respect for

exterior, bodily means of recollection, with a view to practising prayer of a more elementary kind first, and then
increasing in purity and depth later? This question was put,
and the attempt was made; this little book is the outcome.

Yoga exercises are known in the West. In some circles they
are even very much in vogue, where most of the time they
are wrenched loose from their primary goal, which is religious
and spiritual. In India they are linked to a complete philosophy, which is very different from the European systems,
and even to a kind of faith, so that they seem incompatible
with our way of looking at things, of thinking, of living, and
above all incompatible with our Christianity. The fact that
the West abstracts from all this only the purely physical
parts for its own use is, however, due to quite different
motives.

Nevertheless, apart from those who practise Haṭha Yoga
for exclusively profane ends, there is a kind of *élite* who,
being attracted by certain aspects of Oriental thought and
sometimes fascinated by the supra-normal powers of some
Hindu yogis, try to join the latter on the ideological, spiritual
and religious level. Only too often the results are, frankly,
lamentable. Lacking a competent guide, misled in any case
as to the essence of Yoga, and not distinguishing adequately
between the practices of this ancient discipline and its
doctrinal implications, whether Vedantist or Brahmanic,
which serve it by way of matrix, Christians, and especially
young Christians, go off the track, lose their way and run
the risk of falling into aberrations such as the cult of the
body, fakirism, theosophy, magic and esotericism. Others,
better informed and anxious to keep their Yoga training and
their faith in accord, follow up paths that are no less dangerous: introspection, analysis of the subconscious, identification of the true and false self, and so on. Father Régamey
wrote recently, and with good reason, a very forthright

article setting forth the outlook for, as well as the risks inherent in, a prospective Christian Yoga.[5]

It is partly with this in mind that this book has been written. Its primary purpose is to give information about an experiment; but it is also intended as a warning.

After giving an account of Yoga technique, I shall at once go on to point out clearly the fact of its having been cradled in Brahmanism, and then show how empirical theories concerning the possibility of controlling physical and mental being have become woven into a philosophical system that is both atheistic and pantheistic. This allows us to clear away the most serious misapprehension of all, and to lay down perfectly concrete conditions for re-forging a primordial, pure and unalloyed Yoga to suit the exigencies of a thoroughly genuine and living Christianity. There shall be no bastardy of compromise; but only a borrowing of methods, to be adapted immediately and introduced into an ascetic discipline authentically Christian in tenor and spirit.

When the reader comes to the sections following this account of Yoga, he will no doubt be struck by an impression of enthusiasm and even of euphoria that pervades the story of my experiment. I wish to make it clear that this euphoria is real and lasting and spreads through the various levels of my daily life, physical, psychical and spiritual. It is not an illusion, or something artificial, one of these "transpositions" that make one live "elsewhere", which really means nowhere at all. It is, on the contrary, a definite condition, admittedly psychological, but physical as well. It could well be called a "state of health" that allows us to do more and do it better on the human plane to begin with, and on the Christian, religious, spiritual plane afterwards. The most apt word to describe it is contentedness; a contentedness that inhabits body and soul and predisposes us not so much towards the

[5] Cf. *Vie spirituelle*, August–September 1955, pp. 135–51.

experience of God mentioned above as towards the spiritual life itself from which it springs and which in turn it strengthens. It is certainly true that the practice of Yoga makes for increased suppleness and receptivity, and thus for openness to those personal exchanges between God and the soul that mark the way of the mystical life, without becoming confused with the latter. But Yoga also produces a more active, willing and generous disposition. It quickens the life of faith, the love of God and our neighbour. It sharpens our sense of duty and responsibility as men and, above all, as Christians. Let us add, to avoid one last misunderstanding, that the euphoria, the contentedness, and all the fruits of Yoga are not sought for themselves by the true Christian yogi. In his eyes these are means, aids and encouragements towards what remains the essential thing in his life: the imitation of his divine master.

It should not be forgotten that the technique proposed only aims at facilitating contemplative prayer[6] by bringing

[6] Hans Urs von Balthasar, in his book *Contemplative Prayer* (*Das Betrachtende Gebet*), has sketched out a theology of prayer to which we refer our readers. The following passage from it will illuminate both the appropriateness of contemplative prayer and the need for its renewal:

"Many Christians do not understand that the reality of the kingdom of God is eternal, that it does not belong in time or to the future. The kingdom for whose coming we ask in our prayers is not something that does not yet exist and that we might bring into our lives, as we do for other temporal and spiritual values; it is eternal reality. The reality offered in contemplation is the eternal reality of the kingdom of God and it is by contemplation that it becomes reality within time, for mankind and for the world. On reflection it will, moreover, be seen that this is in fact the fundamental idea in Catholic Action. Contemplation must not be thought of as turned towards eternity, and action turned towards time, for then one tears in two what in the Christian is united. Unfortunately this was not seen clearly enough at the beginnings of spiritual tradition, and today, in the era of Catholic Action, it is not always sufficiently recognized. It is not we who build with our own strength (even when aided by grace) the kingdom of God on earth. At the most we shall be able in genuine prayer to into existence the most favourable conditions for true attentiveness to God, in an epoch when everything seems to be making this more difficult and even impossible. Contemplative prayer is fundamentally listening to the word of God. It is due to this that contemplative prayer is written into the great liturgical prayer of the Church. The Christian in praying does not have to search for his own self nor to forget himself in the manner of Orientals, but to open himself to the word of God, for it is solely in this and by this that he can find himself and exist.

make room in ourselves and in the world for the kingdom of God, in such a way that its forces and works shall be able to impose themselves there. Everything that we can, by our behaviour, show our neighbour of the reality of God comes from the contemplation which is that of Christ, of the Church, and ours. But it would be impossible to show forth the contemplation of Christ and of the Church effectively without taking part in it oneself."

PART ONE

YOGA AND YOGIS

I

PROFANE YOGA

WHAT the West knows as Yoga really constitutes only a part, divorced from its setting and its religious ends, of Haṭha Yoga, itself one of the basic forms amongst the many taken by Yoga in India.

Haṭha Yoga may be defined as "a comprehensive system of human culture, physical, moral and psychical, and acting as a doorway giving on to gently sloping paths that gradually lead up to Yoga proper, to Rāja Yoga".[1] "Its aim is to control the body and the various forms of vital energy, with a view to overcoming physical impediments standing in the way of other, spiritual, forms of Yoga. Its object is to ensure a perfect balance between the organic functions."[2] "Its ultimate goal and true end is to prepare man for the acquisition of that repose of the spirit necessary for the realization of the 'Supreme', or for 'experiencing the Divine'."[3] It is its religious and spiritual end that is too often, if not always, forgotten in Europe, where the tendency is to whittle down Haṭha Yoga in such a way as to leave only its physical aspect, and to see in it nothing more than a kind of sport.

In spite of laying great stress on the body and on physical energy, Haṭha Yoga is in fact a complete form of Yoga.

[1] C. Kerneïz, *Postures et respirations du Hatha-Yoga, son enseignement, sa pratique*, Tallandier, Paris, 1951, p. 7.

[2] J. Masui, "Les différentes formes de Yoga et leurs buts", in *Yoga, science de l'homme intégral*, Cahiers du Sud, Paris, 1953, p. 41.

[3] S. Bikram-Shah, "Le Yoga, ses exercices, son but et ses effets", in *India* (a cultural magazine), I, 2, 1954, p. 21.

When practised as such in its entirety, various degrees of
development may be distinguished.

At the initial stage, there are a certain number of "abstin-
ences" or *yama*: non-violence—the yogi abstains from everything that harms any living creature by thought, word or
deed; truth—the yogi abhors lying and duplicity; chastity—
complete absence of any erotic emotion; poverty; and respect
for the welfare of others.

This negative or passive stock constitutes the first stage of
purification; and on it are grafted the five positive virtues or
niyama: purity—outward cleanliness, and purity of the heart;
contentedness—non-attachment to things and events, manifesting itself in calm, joy, a special kind of happiness, and the
absence of reaction to what might be called the pinpricks of
life; austerity of living—never going beyond the limits set
by discretion in thought, word or deed; self-knowledge—the
gradual understanding of one's being and of one's self; and
lastly, becoming attached to the divine, and yielding up one's
being entirely to a personal God.

The inner attitude of the yogi has its outer counterpart in
a series of physical postures, or *āsana*. The function of these
postures is to bring calm to the spirit and at the same time
to strengthen the body. "Their end is to recondition the
organism entirely, from the muscles and the nervous system
to the mind. They markedly affect the whole metabolism,
stimulating and regulating it."[4] The number of these postures
is almost infinite, but the yogis of India in fact use eighty-four,
of which about twenty may be practised by almost anyone.
I shall return to this later.

The fourth stage of development in Haṭha Yoga is breath-
control, or *prāṇāyāma*. "From times immemorial, India has
recognized that there exists a close connection between
breathing and states of mind. By modifying and slowing

[4] J. Masui, *op. cit.*, p. 43.

down the rhythm of breathing, the yogis enter into states of consciousness that are quite unlike those familiar to most men in a waking condition."[5] This breathing discipline is a subtle affair. There are, moreover, a large number of different ways of controlling breathing, some of which are secret, and which vary the time taken for each breath, as well as its rhythm and localization. All these ways are linked up with various postures, or *āsana*. The yogi must master his attitudes and movements in order to carry out the discipline of breath-control.

The highest stage in Haṭha Yoga is a kind of detachment, of self-mastery attained by liberation from the external world. The yogi withdraws; he cuts in some way the knot which has tied his thought to sense-objects. He is no longer touched or disturbed by the perception of things, or by the recurrence of their images in memory or consciousness. This uppermost level constitutes a stage on the way to higher forms of experience, especially those in Rāja Yoga, to which I shall be referring later.

It is clear from this account that Haṭha Yoga cannot be whittled down to a mere control of the body and of physical energy. It comprises in its own right highly advanced disciplines, and an earnestness bordering on the heroic. With regard to chastity, for example, the Hindu masters are explicit: it is impossible to carry out Yoga properly and fully unless perfect chastity is practised. Yoga adepts postpone marriage till they are thirty or forty years old: if they are married already, they put themselves under a discipline of absolute continence. Again the same sages point out that the physical training in Haṭha Yoga simply prepares the body and the nervous system for the accompanying or ensuing spiritual disciplines. In the minds of its founders, and of the large number of Orientals who practise it, Haṭha Yoga is therefore neither the equivalent, nor even the counterpart, of any of our

[5] J. Masui, *op. cit.*, p. 43.

systems of physical culture, however lofty their intentions may be, and whatever moral trend they may aim at fostering.

Western technique has nevertheless managed to divorce Haṭha Yoga from its religious and spiritual ends. The West, disregarding the morality which serves as its basis, and the atmosphere of asceticism and heroism which surrounds it, as well as its crowning spiritual aims, has isolated all the physical part—the postures and system of breath-control—and adapted it to serve utilitarian and profane ends. By making a judicious selection from the postures and methods of training, an autonomous system of physical culture has been built up. For the European, the term Haṭha Yoga merely calls up the idea of a group of exercises with poetic sounding names, varying in difficulty of accomplishment, and on the whole rather bizarre; yet experience has shown that the regular practice of these exercises has an outstandingly good effect on psychosomatic being.

Thus reduced to its physical aspects, Haṭha Yoga consists of the postures, or *āsana*, and the control of breathing, or *prāṇāyāma*.

THE POSTURES

The postures of Yoga consist of attitudes or positions taken up by the body in performing a number of movements slowly in a set sequence. The body remains still in certain of these attitudes for a space of time which may vary from a few seconds to a quarter of an hour or even more. The transition from one of these attitudes in which the body is still to the next still posture must be carried out smoothly, without any intermediate pause, and yet without haste. The whole series of movements is performed evenly, rhythmically and without any jerking or abruptness. Once a posture has been taken up, one must yield to it, relaxing the muscles that have tautened with the effort of reaching the attitude. The carrying out of each posture thus occupies a certain length of time, for it includes both the movements performed in bringing the body into the posture, as well as the period of stillness in it. This period of stillness must be extended as much as possible, but only gradually and without causing discomfort. From the posture one returns to the starting position by going through, rhythmically but in reverse order, the movements performed in taking it up.

Let us consider the Snake posture, one of the simplest of the series. This consists of lying flat on the stomach and then raising the trunk as high as possible into the position of a snake defending itself. If you have just been carrying out a standing posture, you must first lie down. Lying down is in itself one of the first exercises that need attention. Raise your arms and hold them straight up above your head, bend slowly forwards and place the palms of your hands flat on the ground at a fair distance from your feet; the fingers should be pointing ahead. Your body is now arched and your weight is on the hands and the tips of the toes. Now bend the arms slowly and lower the body gently towards the ground, if need be moving back first one foot and then the other. Your chest comes to rest, softly and without jarring, on the backs of your hands. Remain in this position for a time, letting the muscles slacken. You are now in the correct starting position for taking up the Snake posture. You have only to raise the trunk, from head to waist, by pressing firmly on the hands and straightening the arms as fully as you can. The chest is now curved outwards and the head thrown back, while the lower half of the body does not leave the ground. Inhale and exhale deeply several times, a dozen or even more. Then return to your starting position by gently bending the arms and lowering the trunk.

There should be no unevenness or haste. The slow pace of these very simple and natural movements calls for effort on

the part of all the muscles of the body. This slowness shows
the exercises of Haṭha Yoga to be fundamentally distinct
from those of Western gymnastics.

A further distinction—just as sharp and essential—is the
absence from Haṭha Yoga of any kind of preoccupation in the
mind, of that competitive spirit that comes into play in
Western gymnastics, whether carried out in a group or
alone. This calls for amplification.

Western gymnastics works the muscles by forcing them to
tauten and slacken in alternation a number of times, all this
usually to a fairly rapid rhythm. Every exercise involves
performing, skilfully and gracefully, movements varying in
degree of difficulty and smacking to some extent of the
spectacular. The gymnast concentrates mainly, if not entirely,
on perfecting his actions so that the result may be satisfactory.
If for instance he wishes to carry out the Deep Obeisance, he
lifts the arms high above his head, bends the trunk back as
far as he can, and, with something of a jerk, brings the arms
forward and tries to touch the toes with the fingers. Then he
stands up and begins again. Using impetus in each movement,
in a swinging rhythm not devoid of grace, he finally manages
to place his two palms flat on the ground, but never for more
than a moment. Once he has achieved the aim of these efforts
—touching the ground without bending the knees—all his
attention is focused on carrying out the movement as well as
possible, at the highest possible rate, and with the maximum
stretching of the muscles. The idea of "success" has become
an essential factor.

In a group "success" is the reward of the gymnast who
carries out the prescribed exercise the greatest number of
times and with the highest degree of suppleness. If the
gymnast is alone he strives to improve each movement, to do
better than the day before and so on.

This "preoccupation" is not entirely foreign to the solitary yogi, who performs the exercise once only; but, for him, it differs in meaning and value. What matters most for the yogi is the posture. He assumes the posture correctly; without *élan*, without first throwing the trunk back. Slowly, he places his hands on the ground, as close as possible to the toes, and immediately in front of them when he has got used to the posture. At the same time he drops his head and bends the neck so that his forehead may touch his knees. But the "spectacular" side of the movements he is making holds no interest for him (or for his instructor, if he has one). He concentrates his mind on his muscles working, and having achieved the pose, he relaxes, he lets himself go, thus prolonging the relaxation. He does not succeed at the first attempt, but that matters little. He knows that one day he will get there; he will reach the goal in a natural way. In the meantime he pays all the more attention to ridding his mind of every worry, of every kind of anxiety, of everything that might disturb the relaxation of his mind and his muscles. He does not begin a movement again that he considers to have been badly done, nor does he bother to correct his posture. He knows that this correction will come of itself; for, however odd the positions imposed by Yoga on the body may seem to be to an uninitiated person, they are in fact thoroughly natural, in conformity with, and even desired by nature.

The final difference is that Haṭha Yoga is a gymnastic of immobility. All the postures are, in fact, positions of relaxation, and although the movements involved cause the muscles to contract in a peculiar way and to stretch the internal organs, they do not have the sudden effect of shock that they assume in the other gymnastics. Haṭha Yoga makes us think "of the unbroken rhythm of a flower opening its petals".[6] The image of a flower is very expressive and most apt. No

[6] C. Kerneïz, *op. cit.*, p. 64.

other metaphor or symbol fits the yogi better (especially when he is no longer at the apprentice stage) than that of a flower which peacefully and without apparent effort opens out in the morning calm.

BREATH-CONTROL

All modern systems of gymnastics or physical culture rightly give a prominent place to breathing. Good breathing is a difficult art. One of the commendable features in a method such as the Dynam is that it teaches proper breathing to its followers from the very first lesson.

> Sit comfortably on a chair, join your hands and place them without pressure on the abdomen, just below the sternum, roughly where the diaphragm lies. After exhaling as much air as you can from your lungs, begin to breathe in by expanding first the abdomen, then the lower part of your chest, keeping the upper part still. Finally let the upper part of the chest expand fully. As soon as this is complete, start breathing out by pulling in first the abdomen (the part that expanded first) and finish by contracting the upper part of the trunk. Then carry out the same breathing cycle again. After taking a few breaths following this sequence of movements you will feel at ease. However slight a feeling of nervousness or irritability you may have had beforehand, a sense of calm is now certain to take its place. This is no more than one of the most elementary exercises, but it is already enough to show the marvellous effects on physical and moral health of a natural mode of breathing.[7]

These exercises—there are others too—teach one how to slow down the rate of breathing; later they are combined with arm movements and instil the habit of deep, regular breathing.

[7] C. Le Gouz, *La méthode Dynam, cours dactylographié*, p. 3.

Haṭha Yoga, too, teaches one correct breathing. Amongst their other salutary effects, the postures have the advantage of keeping in form and of developing those muscles which, set in three groups—on the sides of the body, at the front of the trunk and in the dorsal region—ensure proper respiration. Special exercises bring these bodily functions under the control of the conscious will. The practitioner of Yoga trains himself to breathe deeply, yet without any straining; to keep the air in his lungs by holding his breath; and to breathe out slowly and above all correctly. It might be said that he attends first of all to the last of these three phases. He practises emptying his lungs completely by using a series of contractions. These are the "flying" contraction, which gives an impression of lightness; the "root" contraction, which starts from the base of the abdomen, termed "root" by the Hindus; and the "neck" contraction. In the "root" contraction, for instance, the yogi, standing erect with his hands joined in front of the chest or gripping the hips, his elbows back, shoulders slack and chest out, expels the air from the lungs by pulling in strongly, yet slowly and smoothly, on the muscles of the lower stomach. The abdominal mass should be pushed towards the diaphragm and lifted upwards at the same time. The yogi holds this contraction for several seconds, then allows the muscles to slacken gently and the abdomen to resume its normal shape. This exercise, repeated five or six times, trains the muscles, which gradually accustom themselves to emptying the lungs at the end of each exhalation. It can be carried out lying down or in any of the postures suitable for it.

Next come the breathing exercises proper, which differ for men and for women. Both begin with exhalation. A man, however, starts by contracting his abdominal muscles which lift up the diaphragm and drive out the air from the lower third of the lungs. Then he contracts the median muscles of

the thorax. Finally he leans his head forwards and drops his
shoulders, expelling the air through his nostrils. A woman
follows the inverse order. The inhalation is carried out after
a pause, beginning with the abdomen for men and the chest
for women. The inhalation should in principle take half as
long as exhalation. This exercise, which may be repeated up
to ten times, is done standing, sitting, or preferably in one of
the cross-legged postures (the Perfect posture, or the Lotus
posture). One has gradually to get used to the muscular
efforts involved in doing these exercises until they are performed automatically. Then one switches one's attention on the
air, smelling it, tracing it, and in a way directing it to the left
side of the body, for example, making it expand more, or to
the right side, or to the lower or the upper part of the
lungs.

These exercises do not belong exclusively to Haṭha Yoga,
except for certain details. That is not the case with the
subsequent exercises, for which the former are merely a
preparation and which bear the name *prāṇāyāma.*" *Prāṇāyāma*
is essentially rhythmic breathing in 1.4.2 time. This means
that if one takes the time of inhalation as the unit, this duration
must be multiplied by four to give the time for holding the
breath, and doubled for the time taken in exhaling. Each
unit here corresponds roughly to a second. Thus, for example,
if inhalation takes four seconds, holding the breath will take
sixteen and exhaling eight."[8] *Prāṇāyāma* comprises several
exercises. Sometimes the breath is drawn in and expelled
through both nostrils, sometimes through each nostril
alternately.

Other ways of breathing peculiar to Haṭha Yoga exist, but
it is pointless to dwell on them here. What has been said can
give some idea of breath-control, as set forth by the yogis of
India and adopted by European neophytes to Yoga.

[8] C. Kerneïz, *op. cit.*

THE RESULTS

It may seem odd or ridiculous or even absurd to stand on your head, and even more so to block your nostrils alternately in order to breathe. To the "profane", the exercises of Haṭha Yoga are always amusing. None of them is spectacular in the sense of having something to show off when set beside the movements and turns of skill of strength in ordinary gymnastics. The Haṭha Yoga exercises are carried out "in single combat", in silence and solitude; what then does it matter to the man doing the exercises if his attitudes look strange or his movements queer, when he derives benefit from them, and they result in a sense of physical and psychical regeneration? It does not take long, sometimes only a few days, for the practice of these postures together with some breath-control to prove its worthwhileness. To begin with one gets the feeling of a general unwinding, of a well-being taking hold, of a euphoria that will, and in fact does, last. If one's nerves have been tense and overstrung, the exercises calm them, and fatigue disappears in a little time. The Full Backwards Bend conquers headaches and the bad effects of too much brain work. The Candle and the Plough take away constipation, dyspepsia, and so on. No more trouble from indigestion, no more sluggishness or nervousness. These healing and restorative postures are excellent remedies for poor functioning of the liver, for weakening of the muscular tissues and of the nervous system, and for high blood pressure. They stimulate the invisible processes in the body and at the same time bring relief to the brain and the whole of the spinal cord. *Prāṇāyāma*, by stimulating oxygenation, affects the circulation of the blood, and releases physical and mental life at its various centres. It "calms the spirit", and its good effects are particularly felt by any emotional person. It follows that Hatha Yoga influences character to the good.

One man, after some weeks of practice, admits he no longer
knows himself, and everyone notices a change in his bearing
and reaction. He is gentler, more understanding. He faces
experience calmly. He is content: the pinpricks of life affect
him less or not at all. He is in command of his own will and
goes about his studies without fear and anxiety. His whole
personality has been altered and he himself feels it steadying
and opening out; from this there arises an almost permanent
condition of euphoria, of "contentedness".

The Hindus explain these happy effects by invoking a
physiological technique (in which by no means everything is
mere imagination), too special and complex for us to dwell
on here. Who has not heard talk of *nāḍi* and *cakra*? The *nāḍis*
are two channels; one of them (but in the "pranic" or ether-
eal body which echoes the physical body) starts from a point
corresponding to the left nostril, the other from a point
corresponding to the right nostril; they cross each other four
times at the levels of the four *cakras* or knots, and finish at
a point corresponding to the sacral plexus of the physical
body. The postures and especially the control of breathing
free the energy of the *cakras* and allow them either to
restore the balance in the human complex, if this has been
disturbed by physical or mental fatigue, or to carry this equilibrium to its highest pitch; or, as a Hindu puts it, "to raise
the reduced quantity of *prana* available [the energy that
gives life and movement to beings] to its highest pitch of
intensity."[9]

Put very broadly, that is the explanation that the masters
and sages of India give of the incontestable and frequently
marvellous effects of Haṭha Yoga. It will presumably not be
of interest to Western adepts of this discipline, but it was

[9] Swāmi Siddheswarānanda, "La technique hindoue de la contemplation"
in *Technique et contemplation*, Études Carmélitaines, Desclée de Brouwer, Paris,
1949, p. 20.

worth mentioning, as the *cakras* will come up again in connection with sacred Yoga.

Let us bring this account to an end by quoting the passage
by that great popularizer of Yoga in the West, C. Kerneïz,
where he describes the aim and goal of the exercises he
vaunts:

> The preservation of the human being in health and
> beauty (for the effect of Haṭha Yoga is not only to establish
> or restore balance of body and mind and to produce har-
> monious working in its organs, but also to preserve and
> even to create physical beauty)—this is the object of Haṭha
> Yoga. While not harbouring the ambition of extending
> your life beyond its normal span as some yogis do, you
> will find, nevertheless, that regular practice allows a man
> to keep youthfulness in body and mind sufficiently for him
> to be taken for the brother of his own son, and for a woman
> to be taken for the sister of her own daughter for many
> years.[10]

---

[10] C. Kerneïz, *op. cit.*, pp. 200 and 199.

II

SACRED YOGA

ITS AIM

'LET the student of spirituality try unceasingly to concentrate his mind, let him live in seclusion, absolutely alone, with mind and personality controlled, free from desire, and without possessions.

"Having chosen a holy place, let him sit in a firm posture on a seat, neither too high nor too low, and covered with a grass-mat, a deer skin and a cloth.

"Seated thus, his mind concentrated, its functions controlled and his sense governed, let him practise meditation for the purification of his lower nature.

"Let him hold body, head and neck erect, motionless and steady; let him look fixedly at the tip of his nose, turning neither to the right nor the left.

"With peace in his heart and no fear, observing the vow of celibacy, with mind controlled and fixed on Me, let the student lose himself in contemplation of Me.

"Thus keeping his mind always in communion with Me, and with his thoughts subdued, he shall attain that Peace which is Mine and which will lead him to liberation at last."[1]

"Always conceiving, 'I am of the form of *Cit* (Consciousness)', with his eyes well-shut, or with his eyes slightly open, seeing through introspection the transcendent Brahman, above the middle of the eyebrows, as having the form of the effulgence of *Sat*, *Cit* and *Ānanda* (Being, Consciousness and

[1] *The Geeta*, translated from the original Sanskrit by Shri Purohit Swami, Faber and Faber, London, 1935, p. 43, VI, 10–15.

Bliss), he becomes of that (Tāraka) form . . . which enables
one to cross the great fear of undergoing the cycle of pre-
natal existence, birth, dotage and death . . . having realized
that the two entities, *Jīva* (vital soul) and *Iśvara* (Deity), are
but the results of Illusion, and given up all demonstrable
things as 'not this, not this', what remains, that is the non-
dual Brahman."[2]

A comparison of these two quotations, both expressing the
outcome of Yoga exercises, with the declaration made by
Kerneïz at the end of the previous chapter is enough to show
the vast distance separating true Yoga—the sacred Yoga of
India—from those Western practices that deck themselves
out with the same terms in mere self-adornment.

The aims of Hindu Yoga are spiritual. It is tantamount to
treason to forget this and retain only the purely physical side
of this ancient discipline, to see in it all no more than a means
towards bodily health or beauty. In fact these aims go far
beyond producing psychosomatic equilibrium, and beyond
the joining and harmonizing of vital energies called up in the
yogi by the exercises. Rather do these aims bring about
coherence amongst the forms of vital energy by making
them the foundation and basic prerequisite for man's coming
to know and experience his true self and, in his true self, God.

My task in this book is not to develop the philosophical
theories (cosmology and anthropology) which the great
yogis use as scaffolding to build up their experience. Good
accounts of Hindu thought have been given by specialists
such as Lacombe, Herbert and Mircea Eliade. Any reader
who is interested may refer to their works. Nevertheless, it
may help to give here in outline the central features of the
"faith" and "aims" of Yoga adepts.

In their view the spirit of man is part of the spirit of the

[2] Advaya-Tārakanopaniṣad, 2, 3, in *The Yoga-Upaniṣada*, translated by T. R.
Śrīnivāsa Ayyaṅgār, edited by S. S. Śāstrī, Adyar, Madras, 1938.

universe, part of God, or, more accurately, part of the "divine
principle at work in the universe". The Hindu with a spiritual calling who wishes to live according to the spirit, does
not therefore have to look above or outside himself for a
first reality, an object of contemplation, and even less for a
model to imitate. He is this reality. He himself is enough. To
see God, to contemplate the Godhead can have but one meaning for the yogi. He is looking for nothing other than himself,
his true self, from the knowledge of which he is debarred by
a whole world of illusion. To understand magic, the unreality
of bodies, of nature, of all knowledge and of every product
of the mind—this is the task that faces the yogi; he must
withdraw and surrender everything. The goal of all his efforts
is to silence the thinking self in him by shutting his eyes and
ears to every kind of enticement so that the spiritual self may
manifest itself to him. His experience does not end, as in all
other forms of mysticism, in an ecstasy flowing out towards
something else, but much rather in a total withdrawal into
himself which has no parallel in any other form of spirituality.
It has been termed "isolation" or "enstasy". This withdrawal involves a loosening of bonds, a methodical and
calculated break, without violence, from everything the
essence of which is deemed mere falsehood, deceit and wind.
Negation of the world, of a universe without meaning;
negation of the body, of physical experience that is only
either pain or factitious, pointless pleasure; and finally negation of the soul, of the thinking and acting self, since everything produced by the mind only serves to thicken the
darkness which keeps hidden from each of us that divine
spark, the only true self in man.

Albert Schweitzer has written about this as follows:

The world of space and time has no meaning in the eyes
of the Hindus. The primary need of the individual soul

is to disabuse itself of the belief that it has something to accomplish in this world and something to expect from it. Since the world of sense is merely a magic game that the universal spirit plays with itself, and since the individual soul, put under a spell, is drawn into this game, it must acquire *by meditation* the ability to realize this fraud. Then the spell is broken; the soul remains at peace and enjoys union with the universal spirit, until at the moment of death the magic game ends.[3]

On dying, the spirit of man becomes truly its self, realizes what it is and returns to its principle of being, identifying itself with God.

MEDITATION IN YOGA

The whole of Indian Yoga may be summed up in one word: meditation. This word calls up in the Western mind a series of thoughts, of efforts to understand, a whole discursive complex around and on a *subject*. This is the work of the thinking mind, and other faculties are called in later to add their seal. For the Indian mind meditation is first and foremost the fixing of the mind on an *object*; it is the silent application of certain faculties of the soul to a datum, the fundamental truth of which has to be discovered and penetrated by close union with it. The discursive intellect only plays a very minor rôle in this. It only intervenes, in fact, to sign its own death-warrant—if it is true that Yoga is, in the words of Saravastī, "the extinction of all functions of the mind, the art of emptying the mind and making of it a blank page".[4]

To be in a position to meditate in the sense just outlined, the Indian must master the body and its instincts. That is the

[3] Albert Schweitzer, *Les grands penseurs de l'Inde*, Payot, Paris, 1936, p. 36.
[4] Swāmi Śivānanda Saravastī, *La pratique de la méditation*, Albin Michel, Paris, 1950, p. 118.

aim of the forms of abstinence mentioned earlier in connection with profane Yoga. Then the spirit must be roused, and the inherent waywardness of the mind brought to an end.

The spirit is awakened in the first place by the postures. These not only soothe and calm the nerves, promote the circulation and stimulate the action of various glands; they also rouse the spiritual energy latent in every man. A complete physiology, in which *nāḍīs* and *cakras* figure prominently, is called in here; but we cannot at this juncture pause to consider it.

The principal means, however, used by the yogi to gain command over spiritual energy so as to meditate is that of breath-control. With this he directs the energy towards the centres where the true self will come to realize its own real nature. The Hindus use physiological theories in this context, too, to explain the beneficial effects of controlled breathing. These theories are interesting enough in themselves, but their foundations need examination. It is enough to point out here that amongst the phenomena affecting human energy, respiration is certainly one of the most palpable, as well as being the phenomenon where the connection with the expression of vitality in man is seen most clearly. It is obvious that breathing influences the physiological condition; and, reciprocally, every change in the functioning of certain organs affects breathing. It also acts in unison with the moral condition. Emotions and passions, fear, grief, desire, joy, anger and shame modify the rhythm of breathing, sometimes markedly. Ideas, too, are intimately connected with breathing: the mind at work is linked to it just as closely as resting or peace of heart. It is certainly not surprising that various physicians and physiologists throughout the world in ancient times identified the energy of the breath with the soul, with life, or with the human spirit. (Breath is one of the three "animal spirits" of the Stoics; Descartes took them up again, and Molière ridiculed them.) Although the rhythm of breathing is an automatic reflex, it can be controlled by the will. Learning to control it introduces a new factor of power and balance into the whole of the organism on the various levels of human activity. Discipline is achieved over certain vital processes; the body, the various "spirits" and the whole world of thought are calmed.

This accounts for the importance given by the yogis to certain breathing exercises, or *prāṇāyāma*, long kept secret.[5] None of them would think of beginning a period of meditation without first having purified the channels of the psychical body (which is supposed to echo the shape of the physical body) by numerous *prāṇāyāmas*, nor without having roused the spirit by deep, harmonious, rhythmic breathing.

The postures, or *āsana*, and the control of breathing, or *prāṇāyāma*, constitute as it were the distant preparation for yogic meditation. Immediate preparation takes the form of repeating some sacred utterances. Then the yogi, completely still and restfully settled in a posture he has chosen (the Perfect posture, the Hero posture, or the Lotus posture), starts to concentrate. To begin with he fixes his eyes on a certain spot, for instance on a point between the eyebrows, or on the tip of his nose. Alternatively, shutting his eyes, he fixes his mind on one of the *cakras* or lotuses of his psychical body: that of the heart, seat of the feelings; that of the forehead, seat of the intellect; that of the crown of the head, if he has already reached spiritual self-realization. The *guru*, or spiritual director, will choose for his disciple the "place" of concentration, as well as the "subject" or rather the "object" of meditation. This object will initially be a physical object, a tree, some kind of fruit, a landscape, or else the representation of a chosen deity in the form of a sculpture or picture. This picture or object or shape is "placed" in the area

[5] Cf. Paul Brunton, *L'Inde secrète*, Payot, Paris, pp. 81, 90–91.

concentrated on, such as the forehead or the heart, and visualized as being there. It must appear there, and one must see it clearly in all its details; one must be aware of its presence as of the presence of a real, living thing.

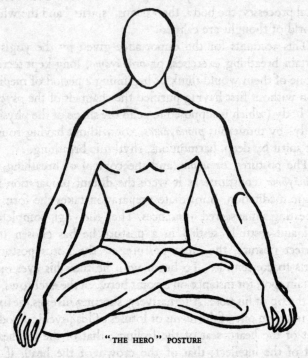

"THE HERO" POSTURE

The whole affair in fact consists of stabilizing and fixing the inner vision, the mind. In order that it may concentrate actively and not get snatched away even for a moment by any distraction, it is forced to imagine or picture to itself in full detail some shape already perceived by the senses. This material image is an aid called in merely to be dismissed later on. Soon enough the mind will call up and visualize at any given point, without external aids, the image of God,

God himself, what he represents—power, goodness, strength or love. The mind will fix firmly on *one* idea, on a single idea growing ever purer, without allowing itself to be distracted any longer or carried off by the moving waters of a plurality of ideas. It will cease being "the monkey leaping continually from branch to branch", to quote a metaphor used by one of the masters of Yoga. It will be "the shepherd grazing his ewes without allowing them out of his sight", or "the man who remains peacefully on the river bank watching the waters sliding past before him".

Another method of stabilizing the mind and stopping it from straying is using the *japa* or continuous repetition of a holy word, prayer or verse from one of the sacred books. This word, striking the ear, or this voice, echoing within the soul, reaches the subconscious mind, seizes it and introduces into it the divinity called for or called up; or, put more simply, the *japa* creates in the mind a kind of growing obsession that drives out every profane idea and in this manner makes for spiritual development.

It should not be forgotten that, in meditating, the yogi is aiming not so much at deeper understanding of a truth or of the truth about the things on which he concentrates, as at the experiencing of his true self. His aim is to discipline the mind and to master it in the way he has mastered the body, forcing it to keep silence so that the voice of the spirit may make itself heard. The objects of concentration, whether concrete or abstract, are not so much to be reached or possessed; they are rather to be used as stepping-stones towards the revelation of man's true self to him. His mind is fixed on the divine only so as to recognize himself in it: "I am That", "I am He". This is the supreme experience, or *samādhi*, where the spirit of man shows itself to him, within him, in its essence, as if he were emptied of himself.

This *samādhi* must not be classed with the supreme intuitions such as Christian mystics have always experienced—St Catherine of Siena: "I am He who is, you are she who is not." Nor can it be put on a par with the highly varied and thoroughly spontaneous "revelations" that the saints have occasionally enjoyed—St Gertrude seeing herself in the heart of Christ; St Francis of Assisi or St Teresa of the Child Jesus realizing their true vocations. With them there can be no talk of auto-suggestion. Yet it is curious that from the time of his initiation the novice to Yoga learns to say and repeat as a *japa*, "I am That, I am Brahman". He induces a state of sacred obsession, and gradually the idea comes to stay. The desires and bodily passions are extinguished, the noises of the mind are quelled; finally the idea alone remains, sparkling like a diamond. The art of the yogi is to establish himself in a complete silence, to empty himself of all thoughts and illusions, to discard and forget everything but this one idea, the linchpin of Indian syncretism: man's true self is divine; it is God, and the rest is silence.

III

YOGA AND THE CHRISTIAN

WE have now set out the essentials of the practice of sacred Yoga. Little has so far been made of one obvious fact, which is important for us: that these practices are linked up with philosophical and religious beliefs absolutely incompatible with Christian dogma. All the great yogis, for instance, take themselves for God or for a part of God, the Ineffable and Unutterable. But the majority of them also worship Shiva or Krishna, or some other deity in the Hindu pantheon. Their thinking seems to be imbued with a double polarity; the sacred game of Yoga is played, for them, on two levels. The first of these is the level of the Absolute, the Abstract, pure Ideas, the undifferentiated One; the other level is that of the relative, or manifestation, of the concrete and multiple. The Indian passes from one to the other with an ease and mastery that bewilder us.

"There is no God but Brahman." But every yogi without exception has his tutelary deity, his personal god, his *īśvara*. The *īśvara* is himself one of the forms or rather manifestations of the great unique *Īśvara*, who is a replica on the level of concrete existence of Brahman, the undifferentiated Absolute; the Being who is beyond being.

This Brahman is accessible only to the spirit. But just as the true self of man is shrouded in all the ego's, all the I's which serve to express our life on earth (I eat, I live, I breathe, I pray, I worship, and so on), it is necessary to place Brahman on a level where each ego may have contact with him, may have bonds and relationships. Brahman must be brought close to us, down to the level of consciousness; in short, he must be made into a personal God.

This is a thoroughly disturbing instance of the out-and-out syncretism found in Hinduism. It sees nothing more in belief, faith and religion than a disposition of the heart or spirit in the service of an ideal, but without intrinsic value. Its point of view might be expressed as follows: "There is no God but Brahman, the Impersonal and Absolute, but to reach him we must act as if the world of forms, the subjective aspects of this unique Reality, were themselves real."

Admittedly this is only one example taken from many. But the frightening consequence is that the great masters of Yoga never stop asserting and claiming that their practices are independent of all religions, that they will fit any *credo*, and suit the free-thinker just as well as the Roman Catholic. It is certainly here that the danger lies in so many books and popular pamphlets in which the *swāmis* of today set out their experiences for us. Whoever can see and read is struck at once by the way their theories and even the principles of Yoga as they expound them are constantly overlaid by leading concepts of a spirituality that is fundamentally Hindu. Yoga, in the school of the masters, seems to have been cast in the religion of the Absolute. It is a brahmanized Yoga, where Hinduism has soaked into the marrow of its bones; it is a Yoga enslaved to a system of thought entirely Indian and Vedantist. The Westerner who wishes to make use of a discipline which in the minds of its inventors was nothing more than a skill must therefore take care first of all to sort out the theories from the practice, and to remove the exercises from the Brahmanic atmosphere that seems to be their matrix; he must then restore them to their pristine condition before introducing them into a Christian climate. Though such a task may seem arduous, it can nevertheless be accomplished. I hope to show this from my own experience.

YOGA APART FROM HINDUISM: CONDITIONS
FOR A CHRISTIAN YOGA

Let us get rid of one source of misunderstanding by sweeping aside a piece of chicanery that provides us with a very palpable instance of the kind of Hindu syncretism we were expounding above.

Some well-known Orientalists see no difficulty in the fact that Yoga is embedded in Brahmanism and Vedānta. A good example of this attitude is seen in Herbert: "It must not be thought that the practices of the great yogis are inseparably tied to the concepts peculiar to Hindu theology."[1] It is therefore possible to "profit from their techniques without giving up any of one's own beliefs". Indeed, "it would be an error fraught with dire consequences to let slip the body of ideas in religion to which we have been accustomed from our childhood, under the constant influence of which we are living, and which teems for us with a wealth of associations. Nothing is simpler than to supply Western Christian names in place of Hindu in the treatises on Yoga technique."

These lines may stand without comment. What true Christian, what man of even average faith would agree to this subterfuge: God the Father instead of Brahman, Christ in place of Rāmā, Śiva or Hari, Mary for Kālī. This is a mere juggling with words. Granted that, as Herbert points out, for Hindus "the saying of Jesus 'I and my Father are One' may have as much weight and meaning as the Upanishadic utterance 'I am That (I am God)'".[2] I imagine, too, that they find no difficulty in reading their own meaning into this saying of St John's: "No man has ever seen God; but now

[1] J. Herbert, *Spiritualité hindoue*, Albin Michel, Paris, 1944.
[2] J. Herbert, *loc. cit.*, pp. 424-5.

his only-begotten Son, who abides in the bosom of the Father, has himself become our interpreter" (John 1.18). Their syncretism allows them to regard Jesus as an *īśvara*; but we may by no means do so. If we want to turn their techniques to account we must first of all—and this needs saying more than once—disengage them from the matrix in which they are embedded, free them from the bed of Hindu philosophy and theology where they have sprung up and flowered, to restore them if we can to the native purity of their original condition.

We shall obviously discard the interplay of opposites, the enantiodromia of Vedantist thinking; also the subtle distinction between Reality on the one hand and its own unreal appearance on the other—the great illusion, the world; between the true and false self; and between Brahman and Īśvara. For the Christian there exist two orders of things, and two worlds: on the one hand the natural, visible, finite and transitory, and on the other the supernatural, the "place" of the divine and of grace. These two worlds are, none the less, though by virtue of different qualifications, both real. Although one of them may be termed more real than the other and therefore justly claim more esteem and attachment from men, this is owing to a hierarchy in which each is assigned his value and objective character. The visible world may be a trap and give rise to illusion; but it is not in itself an illusion, or a vast fraud, or mere air.

The psychology I am using helps us to distinguish several stages in man and in the individual soul. We shall speak of three lives in man, and the goal of "our" Yoga will be precisely to foster the growth, if not the final fruition of the highest of these lives, the spiritual. But in holding aloft this highest functioning of the human complex as our end, we shall take care not to separate and even less to set at variance what God has joined in us. We shall not speak in terms of a true and false self. It is a curious thing that in denying that the "inner man" is God or a part of God, an emanation from the divine centre, we shall discover that close relations also exist between him, the transcendent, personal God and the "I" of Christians; yet they are close in a sense different from the relations existing between the self and the Self, the individual spirit and the Spirit itself of Hindu mystics. They are in fact closer, but in a different way. "I" am not "he who is". I am the nothing that owes him being. I am above all —and this is something quite different—he whom, in his love, he has brought to birth in a new life; I am he whom he saves and knows in his son, first-born of all creatures; I am he into whom he ceaselessly pours his Spirit, whom he invades and sets on fire. I am then neither fire, nor the spark shot out from it; but iron plunged into the fire; a bush touched by a divine spark and burning without burning away; a hollow vessel, terrifyingly hollow but overflowing with his love.

Being Christian yogis, we shall therefore not seek *enstasy*, which would cut us off from absolutely everything that is in or outside us, and from illusion, magic and pain. We shall not seek this sublime isolation where the self claims to do without all help from on high, and in its silence to defy the absolute transcendence of God. Nor shall we place our hopes on *ecstasy*, the bliss that is nevertheless frequently found in the saints. We know very well that only an extraordinary grace from the God of all consolation can "transport" (I Cor. 12.2–3) us, and it matters little whether this happens within our body or beyond it. We shall on the contrary simply strive to discover a little of what God is, and then to feel and experience what we are with respect to him. We shall have to understand that he is Father, and *our* Father; that he is Son, the only Son, in whom however we become children of God and like unto God; that he is Spirit, that he is Love, yet also the fullness that comes to fill up our need, that becomes our own love. We must come to know something we already know from faith and revelation; we must experience it ourselves, after having learnt it from Christ and his Church.

All this will distinguish our private meditation from that of the Brahmanic yogis. Admittedly, we shall come to the idea, as they do, that our God is the Ineffable and Unutterable; but his countenance will be for us something other than the "countenance of silence" spoken of by Ramakrishna. We shall "look on" our God, we shall "see" him living in Holy Scripture and in his creation. We shall think of everything that he is, everything that our Catholic creed teaches us about him. Our spirit will concentrate on *what* he is, both in himself and for us. In bringing him near us, in seizing and embracing him, we shall taste him and enjoy him both in himself and in us. In this supreme calm wrought in us by the exercises and practice of Yoga, we shall be free, relaxed and at one in the centre of our being; we shall be ready to tremble at the touch of the Holy Ghost, to receive and welcome what God in his goodness thinks fit to let us experience. We shall guard against mistaking ourselves for our own light. It will not be our thoughts producing in our soul that completely new clarity, so sudden and unexpected, which is the result—given in its own time by the Spirit, who bloweth where he listeth—of a prayer, of perseverance in prayer. But in obtaining peace for ourselves (*śānti*, one of the aims of Yoga), in purifying our soul of every extraneous thought and of every thought altogether (another goal of Yoga), in emptying our heart at least of everything that is not he, we shall be making our being ready to be taken, to be seized— and this is surely one of the forms, in fact the highest (*pati divina*) of Christian contemplation. Contentedness, this disposition "to accept and never to undergo" in the words of Dr Vittoz, contentedness or *santosha*, which is second nature to the yogi, will help us in no meagre fashion to establish in ourselves a condition where we are habitually in contact with God and where we keep up a dialogue with our Lord, whatever activity we may be engaged in. Occasionally we shall find ourselves repeating the *mantra*, the name of the Deity, just like the Hindu yogis; but for us this name shall mean the presence of the Father (the hand placed on the weak shoulder of the child), the presence of the Son, God the Saviour, and the presence of the Holy Ghost, of Love.

In short, we shall not only remain Christians as Herbert wishes, but furthermore, a point he has not thought of, we shall establish ourselves at the centre of a true Christianity. As for the practices of Yoga, we shall take them simply for what they are, neither religion nor mysticism, but a discipline, a skill, admittedly ingenious. It is the art of *uniting*, of gathering together in man the elements that are too often scattered or sundered; the art of bringing the life of the spirit to open out in him, this life that is more divine for the Christian than for the Hindu. It is the art of *joining*, of helping grace to unite with God his privileged creature—and this belongs to Christian Yoga alone. For us Yoga shall be the *technique* that allows man—when this is fitting—to establish himself in silence; not merely away from noise, but effectively in the silence of the senses, desires and human passions, in the silence of mind, banishing preoccupying thoughts and worries, accepting above all to remain silent so that the Holy Spirit of God may now and then make its voice heard, and the spirit of the man be listening.

PART TWO

A CHRISTIAN YOGA

I

AN ANCIENT VIEW OF MAN

THE HUMAN COMPLEX

THE early Fathers, sublimely indifferent to everything the Schoolmen were to teach later about the unity of the human soul, did not hesitate to distinguish clearly between *anima*, *animus* and *spiritus* in man. They spoke of "animal" (or psychic) men, "rational" (or gnostic) men, and "spiritual" (or pneumatic) men, depending on which of these three functions was dominant in an individual.[1]

This terminology is no longer used nowadays, on the grounds that it may lead to ambiguity. The "modern" view distinguishes three lives, standing in hierarchic relation to each other. The first of these, organic life, man shares with plants and animals; but it is subordinated in him to mental or intellectual life, which belongs to man alone and makes him distinct from animals. This second life, however, seems to be given to man only so that he can raise himself to a third life, which, in the same way as organic life, does not contain in itself its principle of being, nor its springs of life and action. It borrows these from a higher source, the selfsame source that has produced everything and steers everything towards one goal. In the third life, man is released from the yoke of affect and passion, which is proper to the other two lives. The presiding spirit that directs the soul and illuminates it as if by reflection from the Deity is heard when the world of the sense is silent. Nothing can take place in the senses or the

---

[1] See William of Saint-Thierry, *Lettre aux Frères du Mont-Dieu*, Desclée de Brouwer, Paris, 1956, pp. 50–52.

imagination unless it has been willed by the self, or suggested by the supreme power into which the self comes to be absorbed and merged. Maine de Biran points out that this was perhaps the primordial condition from which the human soul has fallen, and which it aspires to reach again. He goes on:

> Christianity alone can explain this mystery. It alone reveals to man a third life higher than that of the senses and of the human reason and will. No other philosophical system has reached this altitude. The Stoic philosophy of Marcus Aurelius, though lofty, does not go beyond the limitations of the second life, and gives an exaggerated account of the power of the will and even of reason on the affects and passions of the life of the senses. But there does exist something further: the absorption of reason and will into a supreme power, an absorption which effortlessly produces a condition of perfection and joy.[2]

These thoughts of a philosopher show clearly that the early Fathers, basing themselves, moreover, on St Paul (I Thess. 5.23), were not so blind after all when they made a careful distinction in the human complex between these three principles of activity, *anima*, *animus* and *spiritus*. Let us consider them more closely.

Anima controls the life of the body. It regulates the bodily functions, and is present everywhere. It is ready to act with a wisdom and skill that is beyond us or at any rate that cannot be grasped by the mind.

Animus is the conscious part in us, the part that thinks, reasons, decides on courses of action, and gives our human existence its personal and responsible character.

Spiritus is harder to define. Its activity is meta-rational. It

[2] Maine de Biran, *Nouveaux essais d'anthropologie*, cf. *Oeuvres choisies*, ed. Gouhier, Aubier, Paris, 1942, pp. 289–90.

is a certain power of loving, of tending towards, of attaching itself; or rather, it is in essence love, tendency, desire, a silent clasping of the true, the good, the beautiful, of God.

We thus have one soul, but three "somethings". On the balanced interplay of these three in us depend the harmony of our being, the unfolding of our personality, and the uplifting of our inner life. The Latin West, always shying at mystery and wishing to simplify things and reduce them to clear concepts, generally forgets *anima* and *spiritus*, and sees in man nothing but *mens*, with its two faculties, intelligence and will. This mind is in opposition to the body and its instincts. Yet the whole matter is really more complex. It is certainly closer to the truth to distinguish, as is done in the East, the three "stages", the three "faculties", the three "hypostases" (it is impossible to find a satisfactory expression) of the human soul. This distinction does not argue against the simplicity, in the sense of being uncompounded, of the human soul, any more than, in one sense, the Trinity of Persons contradicts the divine unity. It is not three souls, but three aspects or three distinct parts in the soul that are here distinguished.

THE "THREE" AND THE CONSCIOUS SELF

It is possible for anyone to ascertain that these three functions do exist, manifesting themselves in three different lives, but also that they maintain a degree of independence from the conscious self of man. If you observe yourself closely, you will notice on the physical or animal plane, for instance, an activity on the part of *anima* that is intelligent, yet not conscious. *Anima* knows how to express certain desires, how to make us take up some attitude without our having considered or experienced it beforehand; some way of acting, drinking, eating or sleeping, which serves, not so much its own pleasures, as the good of our whole being. It has certain intuitive or rather inductive powers. Instances can be found in everyday life. A whole number of reflexes exist that have nothing mechanical about them and yet express this intelligent, unreasoned activity of our *anima*, its grappling with the difficulties it has to resolve. About all this the rational part of man, and his will, know nothing. You are chatting with a friend, and happen to cross a road. Involuntarily, instinctively, you avoid getting run over. A non-conscious self (something akin to what William James calls the "subliminal") seems to act in some way as our double, and constitutes the centre of a whole series of initiatives taken by *anima* on the physical plane, just as happens with *animus* on the intellectual or psychical plane.

Here again examples may be found in everyday life. The brain frequently works at night; in the morning the mind is full of fresh ideas and clear thoughts. A problem on which we were engaged the previous night before going to bed may be solved as we are getting up; even more often the solution springs on us at the moment of waking.

Animus is at work even whilst we are asleep. It is perhaps in silence that *animus* is in closest touch with truth. Hence the advice given to intellectuals: work for the whole of the morning, and rest your minds for the remainder of the day. Do manual work, take a walk, but whatever happens do not think about your morning's work. Not only will you keep a proper balance, not only will you rest and avoid overwork, but you will also be surprised to discover how much your mind, your *animus*, will be able to work out in this kind of calm, this consciously imposed inactivity.

Spiritus too can work unknown to the self. It often goes beyond or before the activity of *animus*. This is fortunate for our spiritual life, which would never make rapid progress if it in fact remained bound to our thoughts.

In ancient times it was usual to read aloud, even when alone. It had been observed that a passage heard as well as read stood a better chance of being grasped. Reading aloud enables *spiritus* to retain ideas that *animus* has not arranged methodically. You may, for instance, be distracted during psalmody, and yet the thoughts and feelings of the author of the psalms may be flowing into you. Your heart, your *spiritus*, will open them to you of its own accord when the right occasion comes. *Spiritus* is often present whilst *animus* is moving about in its own field of knowledge or loses itself in reflections. Clearly, if all "three" are present, the condition is perfect. But this perfection is rarely reached. "Let us pray," says St Benedict, "in such a way that our mind agrees with our voice." This is very wisely put. What matters most is that *spiritus* (which is after all a little more than the *mens* of St Benedict and St Augustine) should be present in prayer, together with the body, with *anima*. If *spiritus* is really there, the distractions of *animus* will be less serious.

MARTHA AND MARY

Animus moves; it thinks, reasons, argues, compares, considers, analyzes. It works excellently in its own field. *Spiritus*, on the other hand, does not move at all; it listens, gathers in, enfolds, clasps and seizes, and all in silence. This is excellence of another kind. To *spiritus* belong intuitions, forebodings, sudden leaps ahead, and plunges straight into the world of the infinite and the divine; also that supra-rational form of knowledge that the ancients called *intellectus-amor*. To *animus* belong clear thoughts, reasoning, deduction and some forms of introspection. The activity of *animus* benefits *spiritus* greatly, but it would be a mistake to make everything over to *animus*. For it is *spiritus* that takes possession of the better part.

You have spent twenty or thirty minutes in prayer. Nine

times out of ten you have spent them in various considerations, pious or otherwise. You come away feeling that you have wasted your time, that you have knelt there dumb and brutish, and racked your brains in vain. Or you may have been assailed by a host of ideas, by a whole storm of reminiscences; you feel as if you had been thrust into a chaos, a world swarming with everything but what you were looking for. . . .

And then, a moment later, you feel an indescribable calm and happiness come upon you, a sudden sense of peace and spiritual well-being. You are not "thinking" of anything, any more than you were before; and you have even less wish to think than you had then. *Spiritus* is speaking to you, silently. It tells what *animus* prevented you from hearing a moment ago. The multiplicity that had fettered your soul has been shaken off, and *spiritus* joins you to the One, to God. It has taken up its seat; it is listening.

It is *spiritus* that trembles at the approach of a feast such as Christmas or Easter. In the bustle and detail of everyday life, where *animus*, swamped, has no leisure to act, it is *spiritus* that carries away a lasting impression, a recollection that is always deeper, more penetrating and vivid. To *spiritus* belongs the sense of the divine presence, of being in contact with things sacred. All this shows the importance of silence, of complete collectedness. At the end of an impressive service in church, such as the Easter Vigil or on Christmas night, one should know how to allow *spiritus* to enjoy and take delight in, and so assimilate, what it has been presented with. This is indeed an art.

In the material sphere, in the world of the senses, *anima* also experiences its own joys and intuitions. Those who do gymnastics—or Yoga—are well aware of that sense of joy, peculiar to *anima*, where the kind of euphoria that comes after daily exercise is felt beforehand, or rather anticipated. The infra-rational inductions of *anima* form the counterpart to, or echo, the supra-rational intuitions of *spiritus*.

IMBALANCE IN THE HUMAN COMPLEX, OR THE EFFECTS OF SIN

Man is thus something linked together, a complex. As such he emerged from the hands of his Creator, and as such he was in fact intended to return to God, with the powers with which he had been endowed in a state of balance and harmony. "You shall love the Lord your God with all your heart of flesh (*anima*), with all your thinking soul (*animus*), with all your spiritual powers (*spiritus*)." But sin intervened; and sin is disorder. Sin is the refusal to obey, the effects of which cascade down from *spiritus* to *anima*: *spiritus* detaching itself from God, *animus* shutting itself in, and *anima* following only its own inclinations. Sin is confusion, each part wishing to find enjoyment for itself, as if unbeknown to the other two parts, and yet wishing to make use of the others to serve its own desires.

"I shall be as the Almighty; I shall know everything as he does; I shall have knowledge of good and evil. *Non serviam*; I am sufficient unto myself." That is pride of *animus*, driven to the extreme; this pride is a disease. Self-sufficiency, over-estimation of one's own powers, is a fever that drains the rational soul of any man.

All in all, there is less danger and less suffering involved when *anima* is wounded—that kind of exasperation of the lower appetites, the sometimes brutal urge of flesh to be self-sufficient. Here again, *anima* is the victim, just as *animus* can be, of a form of pride or over-valuation. Nothing matters apart from its pleasures. *Spiritus* gets trapped here, for it has loosened its ties with God and lost touch with superior things. The lower things entice it, and it takes up its dwelling amongst them. It makes little difference whether *spiritus* dwells in the rational rather than the bodily part. Cut off from God, it no longer reigns over and in man. That is the evil. For man is now divided, scattered, confused, fragmented into a multitude of worries and opposing desires; and he errs, taking paths at random, and groping about for a means of re-discovering God in a balance of his "three".

ASCETICISM, OR THE RETURN TO ORDER

At this point asceticism comes in. Asceticism is an effort to restore to its proper place and function each of the "three", and above all to re-establish between them something of the primordial relationship intended by God, which obtained before the Fall.

Asceticism is a practice that needs bringing out into the light. It is a serious misunderstanding of Christian life to base it on some cult of suffering—a disguised masochism— and of pain, or to preach the destruction or annihilation of the body, and such a degree of mortification of its most legitimate appetites that this life no longer comprises anything human. Some people profess such a scorn—frequently Platonic, moreover—for their bodies, commend such a lack of interest in the most ordinary appetites, and veil over certain manifestations of life in man with such horror that it may on occasion be asked whether they have not taken the wrong turning somewhere, and whether, under the pretext of destroying the "old man" and his desires, they do not often bring to birth another man, equally burdened with desires, or at any rate a creature that is certainly not the "new man" spoken of by St Paul. The danger always lies in making an end rather than a means of what is called "mortification", in making suffering into a goal. In trying to put out the flames eating into one of the "three", they may be setting fire to a stake where another of the "three" is bound.

Fasting, vigil, and any other penitential exercise that is

meant to draw *spiritus* out of the hands of *anima* may result in pride. The "heart may leave the belly", and free itself from carnal pleasures; but if it becomes immoderately attached to knowledge and its pleasures, the gain is only slight, and the evil may be the greater. Asceticism or true mortification means extinguishing neither the appetites of the flesh nor the desires of the mind; it means restoring the balance between the different *affectus* shown in man, and which are part of him. It involves putting to proper order the powers found in the human complex; the "three" must be brought together in harmony to accord with God's plan, with the destiny of man, and with the individual's calling.

Everyone, single or married, businessman or monk, priest or layman, must take on the task—and it is no easy one either—of ordering the life of his "three" in such a way that each develops without detriment to the others, and acts so as to achieve the good of the whole human being, its perfection *in genere et in particulari*, following the vocation that is common to us all, as well as that which belongs to each individual alone. To set in order is not to destroy; it is to discipline, to govern. To whatever state a man has been called, he must needs base his life on the discipline that will rule, order and govern the functioning of his powers and his various appetites. The fact that my brother has taken a wife does not justify his giving free rein to *anima*. On the contrary, he ought to control his passions and moderate his appetites, having regard to his own good and to the good of the family he has founded. Living in continence, I shall have less trouble than he in finding the norm of balance in myself which is to ensure my full development.

A brainworker or an intellectual is sometimes in danger of forgetting that he must exert a strict discipline over his soul as well as over his thought. The monk who considers himself to be shielded from pride and luxury because *spiritus* in him glides loftily up towards the divine runs a very great risk of getting caught in a trap. People on retreat have been known to give way to the prickings of the flesh. The truth of the matter is that no one can be certain that one of his "three" may not suddenly go astray. Everyone must be constantly on the watch, lest *animus* or *anima* move out of its own domain, lest *spiritus* "melt like wax in the centre of the belly", or attach itself to presumptuous or vain thoughts.

Putting the "three" in order, harmonizing their activities and directing them towards the supreme goal of man, towards God, is a difficult task that has to be begun over and over again. It is, however, not impossible, with the help of grace, to reach a condition of balance, where the life of the "three" no longer, or only very slightly, hobbles the process of my development into the human being that I truly am, in the Being who has made me for him.

At this point the path debouches on the exercises of Yoga. Before broaching them, however, let us pause first at certain principles of action that aim at producing an enlightened asceticism; and by doing this a possible source of misunderstanding may be removed.

PRINCIPLES OF ASCETICISM

1. *Gentleness rather than force*

The ancients used to make *anima* the consort of *animus*, bound by devotion and fealty. This figure of speech, on being examined, shows us two points. Firstly, the animal man in us must serve the other man, must obey him and must submit his appetites, desires and motions to the constant watchful control of the thinking man. Secondly, and this is perhaps more important, the thinking man in us must treat the animal man with enlightened solicitude, and by his attention, thoughtfulness and love, win its quasi-natural and spontaneous submission.

Anima is woman; one must know how to win her over. She must be brought, but not constrained, to obey and serve. In asceticism, as elsewhere, more is achieved by gentleness than by force. A will that is persevering, but perseveringly gentle, obtains more from the body and from its animating principle than do force and compulsion. No woman is won by anger and blows.

In this connection it is proper to ask whether the rigorous treatment to which some desert Fathers subjected their bodies was not partly responsible for the repeated assaults of the devil—or simply of their senses—that they complained about. If St Jerome had eaten a little more and slept a little better, the recollection of the pretty girls of Rome would no doubt have excited him less in the evening of life.

There can be no question here of preaching sensualism, and even less of condemning certain practices of mortification, such as fasting, vigils, or sleeping on bare boards. What is being pointed out is simply that, in order to produce a sound result, these practices must be kept within bounds by the virtue of discretion. Discretion is something quite different from a sense of proportion; it is the sense of balance, of the natural order of things, which has been mentioned earlier. Clearly one must struggle against the passions, put a brake on the appetites and rein in the senses. But in all this one must take heed of the requirements of each of the "three", and above all of the hierarchy in which they should be ordered. One must also act wisely; one must persuade rather than compel, one must silence, not destroy. True mortification implies solicitous attention to the human body, a real, living love of *animus* for *anima*; but a thinking love, not a love made up of weakness and sentimentalism; a love that unites, but does not dominate; a will that is constant, firm and strict, but less conquering; a taking up into control, but not an enslavement.

Anima will in any case not be a faithful consort for *animus*, nor will *animus* fulfil its rôle of sublimating partner, unless the latter places itself under the control of *spiritus*, of a *spiritus* attached to God, its principle of being. Perfection, the ladder of perfection, starts at the bottom; both feet of the ladder rest on the earth. But it only holds firm in so far as the top is fixed to or set against something or someone not of this earth. In climbing this ladder, you have to set both uprights firmly against God.

This illustrates once again the fundamental unity of man amidst the apparent complexity of his being and powers. He is neither angel nor beast; yet angel and beast (*spiritus* and *anima*) both at once, with this marvellous connecting link between the two—*animus*.

2. Respect for God's plan

Asceticism is not penance. Penance is an act that does violence to nature, even when good; it causes pain and suffering in the body and the heart. Asceticism is basically an effort directed towards setting nature right again, and re-establishing order and balance. This effort admittedly requires discipline, but normally this is not accompanied by suffering. If it does cause pain, it has generally gone beyond its goal, and may even miss it completely.

Asceticism resides, to begin with, in the heart. It is a constant, enlightened set of the will; for *spiritus* has linked, or rather desires to link, itself with God, to cleave to God, and thus rediscover its pristine condition. For this reason, using *animus* as an intermediary, *spiritus* takes ascendancy over *anima* (instead of being dominated by it) and lays down for it a rule consisting of laws and customs solely aimed at restoring it to its proper function, to re-establish it in its original integrity.

Sin is known to have injured man even in those appetites of

his which are most normal and natural and necessary for the preservation of life. It has struck at and weakened nature even in the exercise of the most noble function that can fall to it: contributing to the work of creation by the reproduction of mankind. ". . . no creature on earth but had lost its true direction"; but all creatures are not sinful. Evil does not reside in things. Fallen man remains a creature of God. True Christian asceticism seeks just this: to distinguish first of all what there is in man and his appetites that comes from God and returns to him, and then what there is in man that arises from sin, what shows a palpable deviation, an aberration from the divine plan and the first dispensation—a leap into the abyss.

Illness and death are the consequences of sin. I must nevertheless keep watch over my health. I must look after myself if I am unwell and take all necessary precautions. I must promote the development and welfare of my bodily nature. *Mens sana in corpore sano* is right enough, but there is more than that in the care I take of my body; there is respect for God's plan and for God himself.

Eating, drinking, sleeping, keeping the bodily functions regular, taking exercise—all this is not merely normal; it is also necessary and intended by God. I have no cause to blush at enjoying glowing health and having a clear complexion. I can be happy, very happy, if I am keeping really well and have no physical complaints. I shall be all the readier to welcome suffering, if God should send me it for my own good, or if, to share more fully in the life of Christ, I should impose on myself some suffering or mortification.

But my body makes exacting demands, and under the pretext of obtaining or maintaining health, asks for more than is necessary. So I seek rest in gratification, and I misuse all the good things at my disposal. . . . This is the consequence of sin, and here asceticism should step in.

This point is important and worth noting. God wished the functions that keep human life going to be accompanied by a pleasure, which in itself is good. But as a result of the imbalance produced in man by the Fall, this pleasure tends to dominate and become unruly and extravagant. It masters *spiritus* and enslaves it, thus placing itself between *spiritus* and God. This pleasure can no longer be brought to order by the voice of human reason, so that it becomes an end in itself and *animus* has not the power to put it back on the right track. Its extravagance swamps everything. Giving in to it only makes it all the more avid. And *anima* becomes its special victim.

Let those who deny sin give what explanation they can of the wretched state of decay into which some people fall, simply as a result of having followed their instincts and appetites. Let them explain the disorders of all kinds, physiological and psychological, which are the sad wages of a gay life of pleasure.

Animals are prisoners of their instincts. In general, however, these instincts are "reasonable" and do not in any way manifest that impassioned and even brutal quality found in reasoning intelligent beings. Man is free, but his instincts and the urges of his nature will take charge of him, if they are not curbed, and drag him down into disorders not be found amongst animals. Why, then, should the desire to eat, drink and sleep inexorably lead me, unless I exercise special care, towards excesses quite out of keeping with the natural order —gluttony, drunkenness, laziness and its derivative evils? It is because I am free. Once and for all God gave to unthinking animals the balance that makes them keep a just measure in all things. They do this without effort, and without thereby winning merit. God wished that in man this balance should be the fruit of virtue. The extraordinary harmony reigning before the Fall in the human complex was normal, but preternatural. It was intended to be experienced and to become quasi-natural owing to the good inherent in the will of man. But the Fall thwarted God's plan and at the same time destroyed for ever and ever the harmony of the "three". No one, excepting Christ and his blessed Mother, has ever been known to manifest a nature that is perfectly ordered and secure from all deviations.

It has to be admitted that the presence in man of carnal appetites under the control of reason and will—and therefore free—constitutes a weakness in the fallen condition into which all the sons of Adam are born. But this can and should become—here the plan of Providence is seen—the opportunity for man to show his superiority and dignity as a child of God. In fact, the temptations of the flesh are amongst the easiest to master—provided of course that the desire to do this is present, and that no physiological or psychological disturbance exists. The normal man is temperate, if he really wants to be; that is to say, if he makes use of the means for this, if he carries out ascetic practices in a consistent and enlightened manner, and if he treats himself like a man, not like a beast, and like a man who depends on God and is moving towards God.

This digression on liberty, inadequate as it is, must now be brought to a close. The first duty of a man, then, who wishes to rediscover his natural balance is to look squarely at the legitimate appetites of *anima*, even if they are unruly. Neither the desire to eat, nor the desire to drink, nor the frequently less noble calls of the lower body are bad or baneful in themselves. That much is clear enough. Nevertheless, how many people are sometimes tempted to confuse order and disorder in this context, and to treat nature with such extreme severity that one would think all these calls, desires and appetites are necessarily suspect and should be dealt with as such. Eating—that is unavoidable. Sleeping-admissible, but it should be done sparingly, and on bare boards. As for the desires of the flesh, they must not be mentioned. This is possibly an exaggeration; but there are many spiritual failures, false ascetics and pretended mystics who started from this position, only to sink sooner or later into the worst moral infamy.

3. *Self-knowledge*

Lastly, one must get to know oneself by dint of inner questioning and patient observation. Each man's nature makes its own particular demands, and each man experiences appetites peculiar to him even in respect of their lack of balance and their congenital disorder. I am drawn towards a certain pleasure, or towards a certain form of pleasure; my fallen nature drags me on into that excess. I have to take care and apply *ad hoc* remedies to the ills that lie in me. What cures my foot does not necessarily cure my head. What keeps *my* nature from straying is not necessarily what keeps my brother on the right track.

Each man has a temperament of his own, and must take note of the way in which the disorder of sin expresses itself in him: what particular form is taken by pride in the spirit, self-sufficiency in *animus*, and sensuality in *anima*. Some faults of temperament exist which, while not directly inclining to evil, may promote or even feed certain disorders, and at the same time obstruct one's relations with a neighbour. There are also good and bad habits. Both of these can help towards perfecting our nature, but they act restrictively by specializing us and thus setting us apart from, and so over against, others. There are whims, compulsions and manias. All of these stem from one dominant fault (unless it is itself the manifestation of the fault), or from one general tendency, which makes for diminished stature in our self. Not only should this dominant fault or tendency be resisted; it should also be profited from. There is no more fertile soil than a proud temperament for bringing humility to flower. On a stock of egoism the most unselfish generosity can be grafted. An ambitious man can turn devoted and ready for anything. In short, self-knowledge, just as much as respect for God's plan, is one of the indispensable bases for Christian asceticism.

Each of us, then, will build up his own asceticism on these foundations. It would be inappropriate here to go into details about this. The forms of abstinence and restraint taught by adepts of Brahmanic Yoga have already been indicated. It is undoubtedly not necessary to be a yogi to admit the need for reserve in eating and drinking, for disciplined sleeping habits, and for a determined, but not a morbid, attitude to the lawful and unlawful appetites of the flesh. All this is already part and parcel of the normal Christian life. The same again holds for the virtues, for fortitude, gentleness, generosity, patience and, above all, for the contentedness already discussed—the disposition to accept rather than undergo—which is surely a form of charity, of love, a giving of oneself both to God and to his works. What in the end distinguishes the Christian yogi from other followers of Christ is the spirit that he infuses into his practice of positive virtues and of restraints. His concern is to make himself whole, or rather to draw the maximum benefit from the unity in him of *anima*, *animus* and *spiritus*, and from the hidden relationships (hidden because veiled by the disorder of sin) between body, soul and spirit. How this can be achieved is what we must turn to next.

THE FIRST STAGE: TOWARDS BALANCE
AND PEACE OF THE SENSES

REDEMPTION OF THE BODY

THE Christian yogi is a man who is convinced above all of one thing: the redemption of his body. It is apt to be forgotten that, when Christ died on the cross, he did not only snatch our souls from the jaws of hell, but redeemed our bodies too. Redemption is so ordered as to embrace the whole, not merely a part, of man; and even beyond man, to include the world of matter, the cosmos itself. The whole of the Old Testament groans, with the author of Wisdom (9.15): "Ever the soul is weighed down by a mortal body, earth-bound cell that clogs the manifold activity of its thought." All this is due to the disorder introduced by sin into the human complex; the antinomy between flesh and spirit, body and soul, shown in and strengthened by the Fall of man.

Everything is changed by the incarnation and redemption. The Christian dispensation does not, admittedly, abolish all the old order, for it is not, properly speaking, a new creation, or the substitution of one world for another. It is, rather, a re-creation, a reparation; a principle of new life is inserted into a fallen and degraded world, and a fresh spirit from now on breathes life into what had collapsed and died. He offers himself to the earth to renew it: *Emittes spiritum tuum et creabuntur, et renovabis faciem terrae* (Ps. 103.30). It is for man to accept this offering and to turn to account the new forces just put at his disposal. In his hands everything becomes or can become a means of salvation. Everything can help him to reach God, to live for and in God. What used to be a hindrance may now turn into a means of living according to the Spirit, for everything is pervaded by the divine Spirit, and it only depends on man to discover, by using the world and his own body, the Spirit "incarnate" in it, the Spirit that invests all things.

The new order—the grace of Christ—can be said to offer peace where formerly war was practically inevitable. In the place of hatred, the Spirit puts love; in the place of discord, understanding. The spirit of man is no longer ringed about with enemies. If he wishes, the world of nature or of the senses need no longer present him with snares; it may instead serve to help him.

The redemption of the body; the redemption of the world. The dispensation of the sacraments proclaims the fact that physical bodies, substances drawn from the material world, become instruments and media of spiritual action. Here lies the mystical quality in the Christian sacraments. The Holy Spirit, the great artisan of the spiritual life, makes use of physical substances to work within the soul. He uses them as vehicles for entering the human spirit. Every important spiritual change that imparts an indelible character to the spirit is in fact effected by means of material substances.

Thus, bodily ablution cleanses the soul of sin. And the immersion of former times did really plunge the man's spirit into the divine world. They are symbols, yet they also perform in actual fact what they symbolize.

"If you do not eat—effectively—the flesh of the Son of man, and do not drink—really—his blood, you shall have no life in you." In order to nourish the spirit and feed the divine life in it, we have to eat. Pretending to eat is not enough. Take, chew, swallow. The body has a sublime destiny, for it is called to feed itself on another body—that of the Word incarnate—in order to nourish the soul that sustains it, and to maintain the deep life of the spirit, the noblest function in man.

In the laying on of hands, the Holy Spirit gives himself. What then is the connection between these hands of flesh and the supreme Deity? My hands, the hands of a priest, are ineffaceably consecrated because an oil, which is also consecrated, has penetrated them and not merely touched, but impregnated, the muscles. This again is a symbol; yet at the time of my ordination it actually performed what it symbolized. No sullying can ever cause the holiness to leave these hands, so often unworthy of the ministry confided in them.

Who among us would have thought that physical union could be an instrument *ad sacrum faciendum*? Nevertheless it is so. Marriage is a sacrament, and even, the Apostle says, a very great sacrament. Redemption of bodies.

All this goes to bear out—on the level of grace and redemption—what has already been said about the unity of the human complex on the natural plane. What God united at the creation, has been re-united by redemption. Christian life is based on an incarnation: that of the Son of God. Contact, union, mutual penetration of the bodily and the spiritual, of the body and the soul, of matter and spirit— Christian life finds its substratum and supernatural dynamism in the person of the Word of God made flesh.

The body may remain mortal, may be a trap and stumbling-block to the soul and the spirit; but none of this can take away one iota from the providential rôle of the body in the dispensation of grace. Every Christian is in a position of benefiting from the flesh and using this "body of death", in the words of St Paul, to live according to the spirit.

PRACTICAL APPLICATION

Once the foregoing points have been thoroughly grasped, it will be seen that no desecration of holy things is involved when the mystery of the redemption of the world is linked to purely physical exercises, postures, attitudes and breath-control; or, to put it in another way, when one seeks to ascend in the order of divine grace and of life according to the Spirit by turning a natural phenomenon to account—the repercussions of certain bodily states on the soul and the influence of various rhythms of living on the depths of the inner life. An example can illustrate this.

To receive the Body and Blood of Christ each morning helps to maintain and quicken in me a hearth for divine life, and my whole spiritual life will be a function of this grace, of the gift God makes me of himself at the time of holy communion. In fact I shall only profit by this "communication" from on high if I bring myself into harmony with God, and if, the whole day long, total communion with the divine will accords in me with the sacrament of communion. If certain ways of holding the body, certain attitudes and physical exercises by their nature promote this attitude in my soul and make it easier to receive graces, then this is a clear instance of the kind of link already discussed. Here, at a personal level, is a practical example of how the body is redeemed.

The same holds good if, in order to make my praying purer, I carry out some exercises beforehand, or if I adopt for meditation one of the postures well known in the East for promoting concentration of the spirit and inner re-collectedness.

In doing this, my intention is not to compel the supernatural, any more than it is to put all manner of acrobatics in the place of dispositions of the heart; nor is it to obtain by mechanical and artificial means what can only be the fruit of a sincere piety and a generosity of soul that appeals to divine Love. On the contrary it is simply to create around me and in me an atmosphere of calm, peace, and silence, and especially to establish harmony between body, soul and spirit so that nothing in me shall hinder the working of grace. In short, I make use of a means, genial in its banality, of recollecting myself in the true sense of the word—of gathering myself together, of possessing myself, of having complete control of myself, so as to hand myself wholly over to God.

A GYMNASTIC OF SILENCE

At the beginning of this book an account was given of the technique used in the exercises of profane Yoga, particular stress being laid on what distinguishes the postures or *āsana* from movements in Western gymnastics. The theory behind these postures needs no further recapitulation, for our present aim is to describe a number of relatively easy postures which, when linked to some other practices, can make up a daily or twice-daily programme of exercises. Presumably no one will be able to run through the whole series from start to finish at the first attempt, although the exercises are really less striking than they look to begin with. A whole chapter on the formation of the Christian yogi-to-be occurs later in this book, and there the neophyte will find all the instructions, in particular how to tackle the postures and how to link them to other disciplines such as breath-control and pulse-control. But with the specific purpose of making it easier to give a systematic account of this training programme, it would seem apposite at this point to describe the whole group of exercises; their performance, duration and rhythm will be dealt with later (Ch. V). Similarly, for reasons of convenience and in spite of the fact that breathing plays a considerable part in the correct performance of the *āsana* or postures —everything related to breath-control has been reserved for the next chapter.

The fourteen postures now to be dealt with have not been chosen arbitrarily. The selection has been governed by the primarily spiritual aims set out in this book. Plastic beauty, suppleness, and even psychosomatic balance matter less than the unity of man, the joining, the composition, or, better, the redisposition in him of body, soul and spirit, with relation to the higher life to which he is called. Our whole aim is to bring calm and peace to the whole being; to make a good and faithful servant of the body; to free the soul from anxieties and problems that are, alas, all too common; and finally to arouse the spirit. This aim governs the purely empirical choice of the exercises given here.

Each of the postures described has one or more variants. It is highly inadvisable to embark on these variants until the basic posture has been mastered and has become thoroughly familiar.

The "equipment" needed is very simple: fold a rug and place it on the floor. With some of the more difficult postures a firm flat bed may be used in the initial stages of learning. When doing the exercises you must be alone and lightly clad, in a well-ventilated room, that is either dimly lit or in complete darkness.

Standing Postures

1. *The Deep Obeisance*

Phase One: You should if possible be facing north or east. Stand upright and lift up your arms straight above your head, palms facing forwards. Stretch up as high as you can, keeping your heels on the ground. The knees are held stiff.

Phase Two: Breathing out, and holding the stomach in, bend forwards slowly and smoothly, above all without making an initial jerk to gain impetus as in Western gymnastics. Carry on until your forehead comes near the knees and your hands are placed flat on the ground, with fingers pointing forwards, and the base of the palms touching the tips of the toes. You will not manage this all at once. To begin with place your hands some distance out, as shown in the diagram. The body must swing lightly forwards; its centre

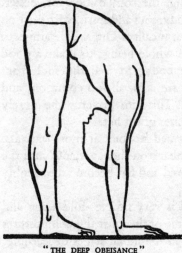

"THE DEEP OBEISANCE"

of gravity shifts. Little by little you may try to bring the hands closer to the toes, bending the head down as far as you can. The difficult point is to stop the knees bending.

Phase Three: You stand up again at once, breathing in deeply. In the early stages you may feel slightly giddy. Your arms return to their starting position then fall gently back to the sides.

Variant: Instead of placing the hands flat on the ground, grasp your ankles or your heels, placing the forearms along the legs. In this position it is easier to make the head touch the knees, as well as to hold the posture long enough to breathe in and out three times, using the abdomen.

2. *The Tree*

Phase One: The arms

"THE DEEP OBEISANCE" (variant)

are hanging in an easy natural position at the sides (phase

three of the preceding posture). First transfer all the weight of the body to the left leg. Lift the right leg, sliding it up along the left, to knee height. Then grasp it and pull it up along the thigh until the heel rests deep in the lower part of the left groin. Press the toes hard against the rounded part above the knee-cap, a little behind the knee.

Phase Two: Stand up straight again, keeping your balance. (At the outset this may be a little difficult; stand near a piece of furniture against which you can lean if necessary.) Then join the hands in front of the chest and remain in this position for a few seconds. Next, raise the arms slowly to form an arch above your head, breathing in as you do so, and keeping the finger-tips touching. Stay in this position for a few seconds, holding the breath, and then breathe out gently as you part the hands and arms, which return to the starting position at the sides of the body.

" THE TREE "

Put the right foot on the ground and carry out the same movements with the left.

This *posture of balance* can be combined with a *posture of elevation*, a *posture of welcome*, or a *posture of offering*. For the first of these three, instead of lifting the arms to form an arch, stretch them straight up as high as possible, with the palms facing forwards. Look upwards at the same time and remain in this position for a few seconds. For the second posture, that of welcome, open your arms, keeping the palms facing each other, as if you were about to put your arms around some-one. The facial muscles must be relaxed, and there should be a faint smile on the lips. If, keeping the arms open, you turn the palms face upwards, you have assumed the posture of offering. Later, when you come to read a little about the symbolism of these postures, you will understand the mean-ing and bearing of these gestures.[1]

Variant: The various positions of arms and hands just given are not classed as full variants of the Tree posture. But when

"THE TREE" (variant)

you have become thoroughly at home with the first version, you may do as follows. Instead of placing the sole of the right foot against the inside of the left thigh, put it squarely in *front* of the thigh, with the sole facing up-wards, and the ankle resting as close as possible to the groin. To carry this out you will have to lean forward a little and grasp the foot with your hands. As you straighten up, carry the bent right knee to the rear until it lies in the same vertical plane as the left knee. (This will prevent the foot from slipping.) A glance at the diagram will show what is meant.

Then join the hands, as already indicated, and raise them, keeping the arms separated. Although this way of taking up the Tree posture is more difficult than the first, it enables some people to get and keep their balance more easily.

When you feel at ease in this posture, try to lean forwards,

[1] See below, Ch. V, pp. 146–8.

to bend over and down as far as possible and to point at the ground with your arms stretched out and your hands joined. Alternatively, still bent double, stretch out your hands and cup them as if you were about to receive or scoop up something such as water from a spring. Make as many movements as you like to exercise your sense of balance.

In this as in succeeding postures, do not be disheartened at any want of success. Force nothing, and do not make yourself do anything again if you have failed at it. Just tell yourself that things will go better tomorrow. To help towards this, think out clearly—at night before going to sleep for instance—this posture and the different movements it demands; this is a very important exercise.

Horizontal Postures

To lie flat on your stomach from a standing position, raise the arms high above the head, and then bend slowly forwards until the hands are firmly placed on the ground, with the fingers pointing forwards, at a fair distance from the feet. In this arched position, resting on hands and toes, bend the arms and gently lower the body. If necessary, move back one foot, then the other, and then, without any jarring, your chest will come to rest on the backs of the hands. Remain in this position for a moment; breathe out completely, emptying the lungs by drawing in the stomach as far as you can. You are now in the starting position for the Snake posture.

3. *The Snake*

Slowly raise the front of the body, from head to waist, by pressing on the hands and stretching the arms as fully as possible. The chest forms an arc and the head is thrown back, while the lower part of the body, from waist to feet, remains touching the ground. The feet are stretched right out, toes back, and pointing in the same direction as the legs. As you

raise yourself on your arms, breathe in through the nose.
Hold this position for a moment without breathing out.
Then, slowly emptying your lungs, return to your starting
position by gently bending the arms.

"THE SNAKE"

Variant: This consists of using the hands and arms as little
as possible to raise the chest; it is the spinal column that does
the work instead. In this case it is preferable to put the hands
not under the chest but by the sides, and to keep the arms
tightly bent; you then raise yourself on your elbows only.
The essential point is to stretch the abdominal muscles
thoroughly and it is to this end that your efforts should be
directed.

4. The Bent Bow

Still lying on the stomach, bend the knees fully so that the
calves lie close to or on the thighs. Stretch back the arms and
grasp firmly first one ankle, then the other. Spread the knees
sideways slightly, and then push strongly against your hands
with your legs. Your body makes a kind of bent bow, while
your arms and your legs from the knee down form the
bowstring. Breathe deeply several times, and, letting go of
the legs one after the other, return to the starting position.

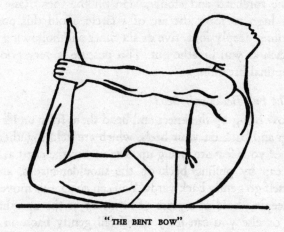

"THE BENT BOW"

5. The Dolphin

After a few seconds (do everything at your ease and never hurry) add the Dolphin posture to the series. Take your head

"THE DOLPHIN"

in your hands, with the fingers enclosing the temples and the top of the forehead, and elbows and forearms resting on the ground. Arch your whole body slowly, supporting yourself on the forehead and elbows, and on the toes. Raise your body high to form the arc of a circle. Hold this posture, breathing deeply four, five or six times and hollowing your stomach as you breathe out. This posture is very good for abdominal breathing.

6. *The Full Backwards Bend*

Now bring up the knees and bend them fully under you; sit up and back on your heels, which are held together; the soles of your feet are facing up. Throw out the chest as far as you can by pulling back on the shoulder-blades, and let yourself go gently backwards. You can check this movement by keeping hold of a piece of furniture or the upright of a bed, or else you can let yourself fall gently back on your elbows. Throw the head right back, until it touches the

"THE FULL BACKWARDS BEND"

ground behind you and you are looking upside-down at the opposite wall. To begin with at least, this is rather hard. The thigh and stomach muscles are stretched to the limit, as are the internal organs. (By separating the knees a little the feeling of strain may be reduced.) You may let the arms lie along the sides of the body, palms down and flat on the floor, or you may rest your fists on your thighs; or again you may cross your arms behind your back, as shown in the diagram, or stretch them out and back behind you as far as you can, so as to expand the chest to the full.

Stay like this for a few seconds. At the outset the tension in the larynx makes it difficult to breathe. Breathe in through the nose and out through the mouth to relieve this.

Variant 1: This consists in sitting not on the heels but between the feet, which are set sufficiently apart to allow the buttocks to touch the floor. The stretching of the thigh muscles is then felt less.

Variant 2: This variant is much more difficult, and combines the Perfect, or the Hero, or Lotus posture with thigh and stomach stretching. You sit cross-legged in the way described on p. 95, the right foot in the left thigh, and the left foot *under* the right thigh or buttock. Then you let yourself go backwards, supporting yourself on your arms which are first held straight and then are bent. The knees must not rise from the floor. For this variant you must be thoroughly at your ease with the seated postures to be described later.

Whatever style you choose when doing the Full Backwards Bend, you should fix your thoughts on the solar plexus or on the pit of the stomach.

7. *The Folded Leaf*

Raise the trunk slowly from the Full Backwards Bend position, keeping the chest well out. You are now on your

"THE FOLDED LEAF"

knees, sitting back either on or between your heels, as at the start. Lean the trunk forwards until your head touches the floor, with the forehead against the knees. Throw your arms back so that the hands rest, palms up, beside the feet. Your body is now folded in three, thighs against calves and chest against thighs. This is a posture of relaxation. Remain thus until you feel thoroughly rested. Then sit down, stretch out your legs in front of you and you are in the starting position for the seated postures.

Seated Postures

8. *The Backstretch*

Raise the arms straight up, as high as you can, and stretch your body upwards. Then lean slowly forwards, breathing

"THE BACKSTRETCH"

out fully and pulling the stomach in as if its wall were to touch the spinal column. Grip the toes with the fingers. Using the toes as a fulcrum, pull hard and lean forward still more, lowering the head. After doing this exercise several times, it should be possible for the forehead to touch the knees. The essential point, however, is to stretch the muscles of the back thoroughly. Now relax the stomach and breathe in deeply, but slowly, through the nose. Hold your breath for a moment, then breathe out; take four or five breaths in this way, counting them. Then sit up again slowly and sedately, lifting up your arms high in a relaxed gesture.

If you feel the effort tires you, take up the posture of relaxation described on p. 102.

Variant: Stretch up and lean forward as already described, but instead of grasping your toes, rest the forearms on the floor by the legs. More effort is called for. The back is stretched out sideways as well as lengthwise. After a moment you will be able to touch the floor between the knees, which are held apart.

9. Posture of Reintegration

Sit on the floor, or preferably on a large, but firm cushion, and stretch out your legs in front of you. Fold in the left leg and put the left foot either under the perineum and immediately behind the sex organs, or along the right thigh, so

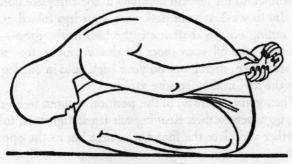

" REINTEGRATION "

that the heel is pushed well into the fold of the groin and the organs rest between the lower left calf and the upper left thigh. Then fold in the right leg, grasp the foot and place its sole uppermost on the folded left leg; better still, insert it lightly between the thigh and the calf. Sit up straight and then without pausing lean the trunk forwards as far as possible, stretching the arms vigorously behind you, right hand grasping left wrist. The forward shift of the centre of gravity will take away or considerably reduce the pain that may be caused by the weight of the body on the left leg and foot. Breathe deeply in this position for a few seconds, then sit up.

Lean forward again and carry out this exercise three times in all.

It is obviously quite difficult. In fact to sit in this particular way needs long and patient preparatory training; but once the knee muscles have got used to this flexing, the position is very pleasant and restful. To train the knee muscles, sit on the floor whenever opportunity offers, stretch out your legs, and fold in the left leg as instructed above, placing the foot against and along the right thigh, and keeping the heel firmly set into the hollow of the groin. Remain like this for a few moments, and then stretch out the leg again and do the same with the other foot. The knee muscles will gradually become accustomed to the tension involved in the complete posture. Try also to work at your desk with your legs folded in, the foot resting on the chair itself, the heel in the groin—you need only take off your shoes for this. At night, too, when you are in bed, stretch out on your back, fold in one leg and place the heel in the opposite groin.

When you can remain in this position without feeling any pain, go a step further. Keeping one leg straight out, fold in the other and place the foot not against but *on* the opposite thigh.

No effort you make is wasted. It took me six months to feel comfortable sitting cross-legged in the Indian fashion, and eighteen to succeed with the Lotus posture: right foot on left thigh, left foot on the right thigh, making a veritable knot with the legs. But naturally I did not have to wait as long as that before reaping the benefits of Yoga.

Inverted Postures

10 and 11. *The Candle and the Plough*

Lie stretched out on your back, with your arms by your sides. Bend your knees and bring them up to rest on the chest. The thighs rest against the stomach. Pressing on your hands, straighten your knees, stretch up your legs vertically, and in the same action raise the whole front of the body so

"THE CANDLE" (Phase One)

that the trunk follows the movement of the legs and forms a right angle with the head. The neck bends until the chin touches the chest. Lift the fore-arms and support the body with the hands on a level with the shoulder-blades, the elbows act-ing as fulcra.

Hold this position for a second or two, and then bring the legs back over the head, keeping them quite straight. The chest curves in during this movement. The toes touches the floor at some distance beyond the head, and the arms take up their starting posi-tion again. The thighs and calves must be stiff. The toes may rest at varying distances from the head, while the extent to which chest and neck curve in also varies. The chin must touch the chest.

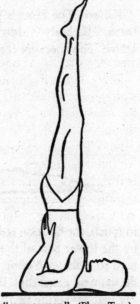

"THE CANDLE" (Phase Two)

After a short while, long anough to take four or five complete breaths, you take up the Candle posture again.

The weight of the body must rest on the shoulders alone, while head and elbows act as buttresses on either side. Return very slowly to the lying position, bending the knees and letting the legs fall back gently.

"THE PLOUGH"

Variant: The Plough posture may also take the following form. The body is thrown back over the head as described above. The knees are then bent and come to touch, or nearly

"THE PLOUGH" (Variant 1)

to touch, the floor on either side of the head, which is gripped by the lower part of the insides of the thighs. This is rather hard to manage. Young people can do it fairly easily, and so do women, generally. There should be no forcing. The arms can help by taking up the same position as in the Candle: the hands on the shoulder blades, buttressing the trunk.

Another variant is as follows. Lie down and stretch the

arms up past the head, keeping them against the ears and on the floor, palms uppermost. The body is thrown back in the way already described, and the toes are placed on the palms.

"THE PLOUGH" (Variant 2)

12. *The Pole*

Phase One: First put a broad cushion on the floor, with one of the longer sides flush with the wall. Kneel down, bend forward and over until the head comes to rest on the cushion, join your fingers near the crown of the head and grip your head at the temples with the base of the palms. The forearms and elbows rest on the cushion.

"THE POLE" (Phase One)

Phase Two: Move the back gently forwards so as to bring the whole weight of the body on the triangle formed by the forearms and the hands. The knees have now left the floor and are not bearing any weight. Then lift the legs from the floor and rest calves against thighs and these in turn against the body. This position must be held for a little while to get

a proper sense of balance. This involves a certain amount of practice, including a good deal of failure and clumsiness. At the outset there is a tendency to thrust strongly from the loins and to kick up the legs, which results in loss of balance and a heavy fall against the wall. You must convince yourself that you will win in the end. At night you should run through in your mind the different phases of this posture and tell yourself that things will certainly go better the next day.

"THE POLE" (Phase Two)

Phase Three: Stretch up your legs slowly, taking care to keep your balance. Steady yourself with your elbows. When your legs are straight, your body is vertical, resting on the head and on the forearms, which form the two sides of a triangle. You have to experiment a little to find this balance and keep it perfect. To start with it is difficult, but after a few months it goes of its own accord. The feet do not normally have to touch the wall, but in the early stages it is advisable to rest them squarely against it. If you feel yourself falling, drop the legs back, putting down one foot after the other.

How long this position can be held varies greatly from one person to another. To begin with a few seconds are obviously quite long enough. This can be increased gradually. At the least sign of giddiness or tiredness, you return to the starting position; in practice this means as soon as the legs cannot be held still any longer. It is mistaken to believe that "blood goes to the head". Granted, the blood does flow *through* the head, but there is no discomfort if the proper precautions are taken: not to hold this headstand for more than a few seconds initially, and then to extend the time very gradually. After one year, I am able to hold this position comfortably for seven to ten minutes.

To return to the starting position, the calves are folded back on the thighs and one pauses for a moment in the position reached at the second phase. Then the feet are brought gently down to the floor.

This posture is, so to say, essential, for it has a powerful effect on the physical and psychical condition, drives away brain-fatigue and headaches; it cures piles; it relieves sexual congestion; it clears the brain and prepares one for intellectual work and for meditation.

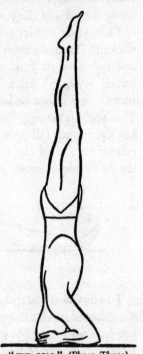

" THE POLE " (Phase Three)

The Posture of Relaxation

Several postures may be termed postures of relaxation. The Pole posture is one of these, for it leads effectively to relaxation. The seated postures, such as that of the Hero or the Perfect posture, to be discussed later, are also postures of relaxation. They create calm; they are restful and soothing. True relaxation, however, is obtained by lying down. Here it is.

13. *Relaxation*

Lie down flat on a coverlet spread on the floor (beds are not really suitable). Your feet are together, and your arms rest along the sides of the body, palms either down or, better, up.

Then you must let yourself go, relax, order the muscles to slacken. The body must yield completely. Start at your head and run over all your muscles one after another with your mind, saying, "Relax", "Slacken", "More yet", "Still more". It will not be long before you feel yourself "gone". The body is resting, limp, "like a bundle of damp linen". Let the mouth fall open and the lower jaw hang slack. This relaxation should last for at least four or five minutes, and the body must remain completely motionless.

" RELAXATION "

To relax well and truly demands a whole course of training. You should not be surprised if the earliest attempts appear to produce no result. Some people find it difficult to let themselves go. But with practice relaxation comes by itself, after only a few seconds, and without any need of giving commands to the muscles to relax. You should order your muscles to grow limp as you breathe out rather than in. Another way of making sure of complete relaxation is to listen to one's heart, to try to feel the pulsing of the arteries at any chosen point of the body. By doing this one can greatly stimulate certain manifestations of life in oneself; one can relieve congestion in certain organs; one can store up energy, for instance, by listening to the heart in the pit of one's stomach; there are many other effects. This is obviously an art, a great

art at that, which requires a good deal of effort and perseverance, and above all deep confidence in certain hidden forces
of nature such as *prāṇa*, about which the Hindus speak.

Relaxation must be practised several times a day. If time
and opportunity are not available for complete relaxation,
it can always be carried out partially. The facial muscles, for
example, can be made to relax, or the hand stretched out and
made limp; or one can sit up, place the hands palms upwards
on the knees, and so on. The habit is quickly formed.
Instead of taking a dull siesta, relax consciously and methodically. On going to bed at night, relax and lie still in the
postures described above; you will fall asleep sooner, and you
will sleep more soundly.

FIRST FRUITS

By virtue of the way these postures are arranged, with easy
postures alternating with difficult, the exercises just described
form a whole which you can with great benefit go through
from start to finish, once you have negotiated the headland
of inevitable initial gropings and hesitation. It should, moreover, be noticed that in their simplicity (for dangerous
acrobatics have been cut out of this programme) they possess
the advantage of making the main muscles and glands of the
human body work. If greater detail is asked for, it can be
pointed out, for instance, that the Snake posture, by acting
on the thymus calms excitement and cools down temper.
The Candle posture—provided, the Hindus say, that it is held
for no longer than three minutes—cures constipation. The
Pole brings on sleep, after having promoted intellectual
work. You will certainly have the opportunity of experiencing for yourselves all these beneficial effects, and of verifying
what has been said earlier (pp. 41-2). I should even be
somewhat surprised if, after some time, you do not notice
in yourselves, apart from benefits of a general kind, some

manifestation of resistance and energy that expresses in its own terms the reaction of your body to the disciplines to which you submit it. At the age of twenty I was very susceptible to cold, whereas now I walk about in the depth of winter with little more on than in summer. I no longer run a temperature as I used to after imprudently over-working. Fasting causes me scarcely any discomfort. I mention these abilities in passing only in order to insist on the fact that they are a means, not an end, and that we should be wrong in laying too much stress on them.

It is one thing, though admittedly an agreeable one, to enjoy good health; it is quite another to have the ambition of enjoying good health so as to pray better, to live more fully up to a Christian ideal. We are therefore less interested here in the physical aspect of Yoga exercises than in the repercussions they have on psychical and moral life.

Yoga presupposes, as has already been stated (p. 32), a whole series of restraints and of positive virtues: non-violence, truthfulness, abstinence, poverty, purity, chastity, moderation, contentedness and so on. Now it is a fact that the exercises and in particular the postures create in the psyche a certain propensity towards these virtues and restraints. At all events they make them considerably easier to carry out. Most of the great yogis are chaste, pure, truthful, gentle, patient and detached, and all this in a thoroughly natural manner; but this does not mean that they have attained this condition passively, without either effort or discipline.

You should therefore not be surprised if, equipped as you already are by virtue of your Christian life with instruction, abstinence and positive virtues, you notice that the exercises and postures set out above bring you closer to the core of this fundamental ascetic discipline and lessen the burden of keeping to it, making it easier, more spontaneous, and above all more natural.

You will feel that gentleness and sympathy come more readily. You will not feel like venting your spleen on others as frequently as before, and if it should occur, you will regret it all the more. You will make a kind of pact of non-violence with yourself, though this will not preclude your having to keep watch over yourself. You will still have fits of impatience often enough, and even of anger. But something will be telling you that this is not only bad but even useless, and that it really is not worth the trouble to fly out and get beside yourself for nothing.

A great need for sincerity will bring you to detest, more than others do, not only lying but also all forms of duplicity or dissimulation. You will sense the more keenly whatever is not genuine, and even what is merely conventional in speeches and words, and also in attitudes that men think they can take up in order to edify, but more often take up lest they should lose face. You will find that you are exacting towards yourself, others, your superiors and directors. You should be on your guard against scorn of conventions, whether worldly or otherwise. Sometimes you have to come to terms with your neighbour. Christian charity must here, when need be, bring back on to course what is in danger of swinging off and unconsciously curving about into the beginnings of egoism.

This sincerity and love of truth will help you to remain chaste. Chastity is in the first place uprightness. It implies respecting oneself, others, God and his plan. It abhors all the compromises that are the replies of *animus* (thinking man) to the calls and suggestions of *anima* (animal man, such as he has become owing to sin). Chastity is aware of the appetites of the flesh and does not despise them, but looks at them squarely and sees them for what they are. On meeting with lewdness, a chaste man does not conceal from himself any of those aberrations which mark only too often the very instincts of the most noble persons of fallen creation. For he knows, and has no intention of being deceived.

Granted that temptation—this pricking of the flesh which makes us incontestably men, virile and courageous—will assail you more than once. But it will be worsted; for the exercises make first for clarity, then for purity. They do in fact make it easier to practise the virtue of chastity.

They do the same for other virtues too, for strength of mind, detachment, humility and constancy. On each of these it is impossible to dwell, the more so as it is necessary to discuss another characteristic condition produced by Yoga, contentedness.

I have already defined the contentedness in ascetic disciplines of Yoga several times by quoting the aphorism of Dr Vittoz: "a propensity to accept rather than undergo". It is thus a disposition that gives the strength of mind and the courage to accept life as it really is, events and things, together with whatever they may contain that is hard, painful or disappointing. It is not apathy; it is more than a "philosophy". One keeps calm and lives in peace; above all, one adapts oneself and with a light heart draws benefits from discomfitures, annoyances and mishaps. One "wants everything that happens to one", to quote Dr Vittoz once again.

On returning from town, where I have been walking the pavements for nearly the whole of the morning, I see when I reach Station A that the bus for B left five minutes ago according to the schedule. Shall I wait for next bus? No, I shall walk. Formerly, and not so long ago, I should have inveighed against these stupid time-tables, and would have soon worn myself out in hitching lifts. Today I walk, lightly, with a smile on my lips, seeing as if for the first time the well-known countryside. I reach my destination no more tired than if I had covered the five-mile stretch sitting in a bus.

What I have done is a perfectly simple matter, which on examination is seen to be thoroughly straightforward and sensible. I am not so sure, however, that it would previously have seemed so easy and natural. This is only meant to exemplify, in a very plain fashion, a certain habit of the soul, an ease in putting trust in life and an aptitude for seeing more clearly the expression of God and his will in what happens to me.

This contentedness that takes up its dwelling in me is a readiness to receive, but not a form of passiveness and even less of hebetude. This silence in me of the senses and of the passions, those parasites that disturb the harmony of my being, leaves me free without exempting me from any effort or discipline. I have as before to solve many problems, to be watchful, to choose, to act—in one word, to will. More open and "abandoned", I feel all the more keenly the need for repeating to the Lord: "Thy will be done". Calmer, more master of myself, I feel my desire increasing to follow Christ and imitate him, who is the essential foundation of my life.

If it were necessary to sum up in one word the satisfying effects of the postures, I should say that once they have been introduced into our daily life as an ascetic discipline, they lead us to an almost perfect *composure*. On the physical level they calm and harmonize the vital energies; they relax the nerves and soothe the senses. Under their action the body becomes incontestably more docile. *Anima* becomes the humble and devoted spouse of *animus*.

The psyche is the first to benefit from this harmony. But by making the soul merge completely into the attitudes of the body, the postures gradually install *animus* in his rôle as protecting husband, attentive rather than dominating. The result of this is a composition, an attunement, a unity which rebounds deeply on the inner life, and which prepares man to rise up and grow in breadth and stature on the plane of the spirit.

In all this there is no magic, but simply setting into action the means placed in us by the wisdom of the Creator. The first thing about it all is that grace—which never asked better than to bring nature to fulfilment—turns the harmony thus established to marvellous account, and that man, more balanced and healthier in body and mind, becomes more receptive and fitter for God, as well as more dynamic, more able to shoulder his responsibilities and duties as a Christian.

III

THE SECOND STAGE: BREATH-CONTROL
AND MENTAL DISCIPLINE

A SECOND ART

THE thinking soul must in prudence behave in its retreat like the prudent father of a family in his home. The flesh which it must rule should not be at its hearthside like the quarrelsome woman spoken of by Solomon (Prov. 21.9), but should be a wife with a habitual disposition to sobriety, ready to obey and work, trained to welcome hunger as well as sateity, plenty as well as poverty on all occasions. The external senses should not be masters of the soul, but its servants; and the internal senses should be both wise and active. The whole family or household of its thoughts should be so ordered and disciplined that it can say to one 'Go' and it goes, to another 'Come' and it comes, and to the body 'Do this' and it does so without demur."[1]

The author of these lines knew nothing about Yoga. Nevertheless, he understood that self-possessedness described above as one of the goals, indeed the principal goal, of this ancient discipline. In it he saw the perfection of what he called "animal man", a perfection that admittedly is rarely won so firmly that it becomes stably fixed; but is none the less accessible, if not to all, at least to many. It is a normal, though not an essential, prerequisite for making progress in the state of perfection, properly called: the unfolding in us of the inner man.

Even if Yoga were taken up only to reach this ideal, it

[1] Guillaume de Saint-Thierry, *Lettre aux Frères du Mont-Dieu*, ed. J. Déchanet, Desclée de Brouwer, Paris, 1956, p. 89.

would not be a waste of time. In fact some people would be
wise to go no farther and not entertain the ambition of turning their yogic experience to any account beyond that of
becoming aware of the distinctive physical or psychical
effects of the postures or *āsana*.

We have already seen how the latter are connected with
breath-control, the second art of the yogi. Each posture goes
with a definite rhythm of breathing, which comes of its own
accord once the pose has been correctly assumed, and gradually becomes more firmly fixed. All this needs to be kept in
mind and watched.

Again it is good and even necessary to prepare the organism
for this particular rhythm. One must be properly informed
about the various ways of breathing, and one should have
experimented with and trained oneself in the whole cycle
and process of breathing. The ABC of Yoga is learning to
breathe properly.

There are two ways of breathing; one for men, the other
for women. A woman's breathing begins by expanding the
upper chest. The lungs fill, starting from the top. Then the
expansion lifts the lower ribs, and finally the abdominal
muscles swell slightly and lower the diaphragm a little. A
man's breathing follows the opposite pattern. It is primarily
abdominal, for the man begins his breath from below. Then
the inhaled air fills the middle and upper chest; the latter
scarcely lifts at all, unless a deep breath is taken. There is no
need to philosophize on the various ways of breathing and
their physiological causes. The wasp-waist corset our grand-
mothers used to wear has sometimes been blamed for
women's habit of breathing with the chest; but in that case
it remains to be explained why, now that this encumbrance
has disappeared, women can only breathe comfortably by
lifting their chest first. It should also be noted that a woman's
breathing rhythm is a good deal more rapid than a man's.

We shall dwell for a moment on these details, for most handbooks represent abdominal breathing as specifically yogic. To be sure, this is partly true, in so far as Yoga is practised in India almost only by men. It would surely be mistaken for the female apprentice to Yoga to modify the normal laws of nature and to impose on herself a male style of breathing. Two distinct systems of apprenticeship in breath-control are now given.

For men

Sit well back on a chair, keeping the body straight like an Egyptian statue with ut leaning back. Place your hands on your knees, palms up. Look straight ahead without focusing on anything. Say silently or in a low voice, "I am going to breathe, slowly and deeply". Then empty your lungs completely by drawing the stomach gently in by a series of slight contractions; later this can be done in one smooth, continuous movement. Expel the air through the nostrils or the mouth, but do so imperceptibly, keeping the lips only slightly apart. This first phase in yogic breathing is of great importance.[2]

Close the lips, and let the abdomen return to its normal shape, the air entering by the nostrils. Go even further, and try to press down the diaphragm towards the abdomen. I say "try", because at the start the habit of breathing either just anyhow or like an athlete—stomach in, chest out—can make this fundamental movement difficult or even a little painful. The sternum should not lift, or if it does, only slightly. The lungs thus fill from below upwards.

At the outset do not try to hold your breath and prolong the apnoea with the lungs full. Breathe out at once, compressing the abdomen and raising the diaphragm as high as you can.

Do this exercise seven times at the open window, at night

[2] See above, p. 39.

for instance, before putting on your night clothes, or in the morning immediately after washing. What in fact matters is that the stomach must be unhampered, with nothing nipping in at the waist.

As soon as you have become familiar with this kind of purely abdominal breathing, you will take care to link up each of the *āsanas* with a complete cycle of deep, controlled breathing. A few concrete examples later in this book (pp. 137–8) will serve to put you at your ease in this rather subtle but very important art of breath-control.

For Women

Keep what is for you the normal and natural manner of breathing. Sitting down or standing up, inflate the chest, raising the shoulders slightly. Then go further so that air fills the middle part of the thorax and the very base of the lungs. To breathe out, start from the top by lowering the shoulders, and end by drawing in the stomach a little. Your exercises, which differ greatly from those for men, are aimed at expanding the chest as much as possible, and at slowing down the rate of breathing slightly, so as to make the diaphragm more supple. After some time you should be able to carry out one or other of the contractions described on pp. 39–40. But your breathing will always remain primarily a breathing of the thorax; it will never be exclusively abdominal.

SYNTHESIZED BREATHING RHYTHMS

The art of breathing well is only a stage. There is another kind of breath-control that is more powerful but also more intricate, more specifically yogic. It calls for great care and for more circumspection than the postures. You can only take it up with impunity if your heart is in good condition. Even then you must move slowly forward, without forcing anything.

Let us assume that you are in good health. In this exercise you should make use of the general lack of tension that goes with the posture of complete relaxation.[3] You are lying quite still flat on your back, with your eyes closed; you are in a condition, not of torpor, but of abandonment. You are thinking of nothing. It is necessary to be quite clear about this: you are not actively thinking about anything. You are listening to your own breathing; or you are following, soberly and with restraint, the beating of your heart.

Raise the right arm in a sweeping gesture and bring your hand to your face. Close the *right* nostril with the right thumb and breathe in vigorously (but without straining) and continuously through the *left* nostril, counting from one to three in your head as you inhale. Then shut the left nostril at once—the right remains shut—with the little finger and the ring-finger and hold your breath for the apnoea, counting again without any hurry up to twelve. Keeping the *left* nostril shut, release the right and breathe out, counting up to six at the same rate. Then breathe in again through the same nostril, counting to three; close it and hold your breath for twelve counts; release the left nostril and breathe out for six counts. You have now gone through one complete cycle—a *prāṇāyāma*. Carry straight on until you have done five cycles, always beginning and ending with the left nostril.

To begin with, it is as well to go no further. Your arm falls back and you remain for a short while in the posture of relaxation.

Later, after some months, you will be able to adopt the rhythm 4 : 16 : 8 and then 5 : 20 : 10, 6 : 24 : 12 and so on, and you will carry out these exercises not lying down but in one of the crouching positions to be described below, either after the postures or in the posture of relaxation, in No. 13 above.

[3] See above, p. 102.

These exercises must be carried out with studied slowness. Progress will in fact come of itself.

Once you have become familiar with this kind of exercise, you can make variations to obtain different results. During the very first inhalation, concentrate, for instance, on filling the base of the left lung. With your mind you follow the air that fills and swells out the left side; and during the apnoea, releasing the pressure, you let the air spread all through the left lung. On the second inhalation, your thoughts turn to the base of the right lung; this is followed by the upper parts of the lungs, first the left, then the right. You should feel the corresponding shoulder and shoulder-blade lifting. Finally you aim at filling both lungs at once. These particular exercises, which should only be undertaken with caution and after many months of previous practice at breath-control, develop the muscles—for instance, those on the sides of the body—which work when you are breathing in and out.

FROM BREATH-CONTROL TO THOUGHT AND PRAYER

However odd the exercise of alternate rhythmic breathing or *prāṇāyāma* may appear to be, it nevertheless produces far-reaching effects, but only, of course, after it has been practised for some time. It calms and soothes even more than the exercises described earlier. In particular it brings a striking feeling of plenitude. It sweeps out and bears away any excitement or anxiety or restlessness that was not touched by the other postures. You feel detached, freer, able to reflect and especially to focus your attention steadily, calmly and effortlessly on a subject or an idea. Alternate breathing is an excellent preparation for spiritual concentration, to which I shall return later.

It is also a thorough re-education of the breathing rhythm, and this is a point that should not be neglected. To make yourself breathe in and out through one nostril—especially through the left, which is very often blocked and not work- ing—is to compel yourself to breathe twice as slowly as usual, and therefore more deeply, so that the air has time to reach every cell in the lungs. Owing to the apnoea, when the breath is retained, a thorough and effective oxygenation can take place. It stimulates the circulation of the blood, whence the impression of warmth after the exercises, a defence against cold. Finally, it ensures all the beneficial results of a gentle, measured exhalation.

The exercises are done morning and evening, with another session, if possible, some time during the middle of the day. After some days you will notice that your breathing has undergone a fundamental change. You will catch yourself unconsciously making the counts longer for each stage of breathing. To the three already mentioned—inhalation, apnoea, exhalation—you automatically add a fourth, where the breath is held with the lungs empty. This promotes contemplation—except when it is contemplation itself that has called for or caused this holding of the breath—that silent gaze of admiration that is poised on a thing.

To breathe calmly and steadily is also to think. So if you find yourself compelled to deal with some important matter or to take some decision, or face some difficulty, do not hesi- tate to carry out some *prāṇāyāmas* first. If you have neither the time nor the opportunity to withdraw from the gaze of men to carry out the movements of *prāṇāyāma*, just do some other kind of synthetic breathing, "squared" breathing for example, where the four phases of breathing (in, hold, out, hold) are of equal duration; or simply breathe out fully several times—for, in all this, breathing out is of greater importance than breathing in. Your ideas will become clearer, your will firmer, your judgement keener.

Suppose something is troubling you; you are anxious or

worried. Calm yourself. Sit squarely and straight up on a chair without leaning against the back, put your hands flat on your knees in the manner of an Egyptian statue, and breathe gently but deeply, repeating in your mind some calming phrase you have chosen. After a few minutes, I promise you, things will be looking better.

The same technique can be used if you are feeling angry, irritated or in a bad humour.

But it is especially in prayer and with reference to prayer that you will feel the benefits of rhythmic or synthetic breathing, because in one and the same action it unites body and soul, the latter being in control of and following up a phenomenon that is normally automatic and purely physical.

Prayer presupposes pure thinking and discipline of the mind, which the person praying tries to withdraw from outside impressions, as well from the waves rolling in from the subconscious, to focus it on a certain point; and all this is carried out where contact with the Lord can be established in peace and silence. What a thankless and difficult task! The mind is, by definition, something that moves, that moves itself across the fields of memory and of knowledge to work on those associations of ideas out of which thought springs, and to make deductions and inductions. The mind is a pilgrim, but never very far from becoming a wanderer, from going off the track, forgetting the goal, losing itself in the undergrowth of confused and disorderly images. Even when it has reached the end of its searching and possesses what it has sought, the mind remains restless. At the slightest invitation it sets off again on its wanderings.

All the masters of prayer dwell much on the way to keep away distractions and to prevent the mind from moving away from God once it has been focused there. But this, which may be called the negative side of the problem, is given too much attention. It is too little realized that in order

to prevent the attention of a person praying from moving
about, aside and away, and from falling into the trap of
distractions, undoubtedly the best method is to attach it first
of all more firmly and wholly to the object of his prayer,
as one ought to God. To pray well, one must first be self-
possessed, in control of oneself, and calm. To reach this
state, nothing works better than the postures spoken of above,
and especially breath-control.

If you are a priest, before saying Office try to base the
rhythm of your breathing on the beating of your heart. Feel
your pulse, and allow three beats for inhalation, six for
exhalation, with or without a pause of three beats between
each of these. You will feel calmed, but, more important,
this exercise will "distract" you and you will find less difficulty in leaving behind your usual cares at the entrance to the
sanctuary. It will fashion you into a soul of prayer. It will
re-fashion you yourself, by uniting in you Martha and Mary
—*animus*, the conscious I, that will have to pay attention to
the psalmody and presumably busy itself a little, and *spiritus*,
the subconscious which has been called on to gather in a
harvest and store it, as if to maintain the zeal of its companion.

Some will find this kind of introduction to prayer, whether
choral or otherwise, too simple and almost vulgar. It is, to be
sure, a humble means, but it works, much better, in fact, than
one would think. It illustrates, once again, the unity of man
and the sublime destiny of the body, since this composition
of the two "I's", of *animus* and *spiritus*, with a view to purer
prayer is the result of a physical phenomenon in which the
body marvellously fulfils its servant rôle.

The body will keep on playing this rôle throughout
prayer, especially in choral prayer, where the movements and
attitudes play a part that unfortunately all too few are aware
of. To realize this, you only have to open your eyes. The
Christian yogi suffers from this state of affairs. For when he

bows deeply, he does so with his whole being; and he feels intensely the value and meaning of these actions termed "liturgical". The influence of the postures does in fact go as far as this; for the man who practises them in the spirit already described, they restore the meaning of the liturgical actions, of all the movements and attitudes of the body, which are supposed to express an inner feeling, an attitude of soul, but which are for the most part robbed of all content by routine. The yogi feels something like an instinctive horror for these dead gestures: the sign of the cross done anyhow, half-hearted genuflections, kneelings omitted, bows called "deep" that are in fact nothing of the sort. Something tells him (*patitur*) that these movements have no meaning unless they are properly carried out. Then and only then do they really embody a state of soul, and even by themselves constitute a prayer: a gesture of love, reverence, adoration, abandonment. Moreover, he is aware (*patitur*) that these gestures, when properly performed, recall the mind and rouse the spirit. This is the counterpart of the embodiment just mentioned, for the gestures here impose an attitude on the spirit as well as on the mind. And just as a gentle exhalation or the voluntary suspension of breathing halts in some way the activity of thinking in order to focus the attention of the heart more thoroughly, so the attitude of the body often restrains and immobilizes the mind, in order to allow the spirit to move more freely along its own path.

IV

THE THIRD STAGE: SILENT MEDITATION

LOVE AND SILENCE

LOVE is the way of the spirit. Love is an attachment that is active and passive at the same time. It is a gift one makes of oneself, but it is perhaps even more a welcome and an unstinting opening of one's whole being to someone or something. In so far as the action of a man manifests his love, the roots of this action draw from some form of contemplation. Because first of all one receives, because one accepts and respects in true inwardness and in silence the will of another who is recognized to be better and greater—pre-eminently God—one goes out of oneself to carry out the will of this other. Love can be said to unite in a kind of circumincession, in a wonderful exchange, on the one hand the admiration and generosity of the lover, the flowing out of his own self in the service of another, with the presence of this other, a presence that is recognized and enjoyed in the "I", in the core of his being.

Love may also be defined in terms of the commandment: "Thou shalt love the Lord thy God with thy whole heart and thy whole soul and thy whole mind" (Matt. 22.37).

For love dwells primarily in the *heart*, in this deep authentic self of man, often called *spiritus*: that very core of the human soul, fine-spun, slender and somehow impalpable. It dwells there in silence, motionless, but radiating light and warmth.

Love is in the acting soul (the *anima* of the Bible). Here it expresses itself in service and obedience, the way man gives himself to his sovereign master, an irrevocable act of generosity, the gift of his whole being.

Finally love is in thinking. Love is not unconsidered, unreflecting sentiment. Its abundant generosity, its attentiveness, the very ingenuity of its discoveries prove that the thinking soul (*animus, mens* in the Bible) has its own great part to play in the genesis, conduct and elaboration of love.

In short, love takes up the whole of man, but especially that noblest, deepest and most personal part of man that we have called *spiritus*. It is in fact by love, and along the path of love, that the spirit mounts towards its destiny and that man truly fulfils himself, as much on the natural plane as on the supernatural that is his by virtue of being a Christian. It is through love in particular that he strengthens his worthiness to be a child of the Father, that he lives up to his vocation as a member of the Son of God, that he grows up and matures in the Spirit—the whole spiritual life. All this by the love that has been deposited in him, with grace; love which is like a seed and which it is for him alone to bring to germinate and to bear fruit.

Who is there that does not sense all this? Whose spirit does not feel it is made to love, to love God in the twofold manner set out above—first in possession, in welcoming, and then in giving? But who also does not feel and experience every hour of the day how difficult it is to love in this poor world? How barriers block the spirit when one would wish it to flow out in generosity and love. How often one is painfully turned back on oneself, at the very moment of giving. How insistently created things solicit and sidetrack one's attention, how they make mush of one's noblest aspirations! How many noises there are in man and around him that set themselves against the peaceful enjoyment of the loved One, and against those moments of rest in the Lord which both stimulate and sustain the spirit!

If calm is needed for thinking, silence is needed for love —the silence of body and heart. That is why the Christian yogi strives to calm himself, to create in himself a zone of silence and recollectedness. This task is without any doubt meant for love, for all forms of love, but especially for that form that expresses itself in divine contemplation, in welcome of the Truth, in a firm grasp of the sovereign good, in final enjoyment of him who is essentially in himself love and consuming fire.

CHRISTIAN CONTEMPLATION AND HINDU TECHNIQUE

We have already asked the yogis for many secrets, but we have not yet gone right to the heart of their technique—the art of meditation.

Yogic meditation is the keystone and, as it were, the synthesis of the whole system. More than any other exercise, it joins, unites, composes the different parts of man. Even this is to say too little; for it is a joining, a composition, a perfected union of the "three" so as to make possible the experience of a form of perception that is truly contemplation whatever its object may happen to be.

The object for the Hindu is the *nature* and *essence* of his true self, a cosmic force and, as such, part of God. For the Christian the object will be the *existence* and *nature* of his bonds with the Lord, the presence of a Deity offering himself to him, to his love, after having made him a participator in his being and his life. These two objects are very different; the starting and finishing points of each are entirely dissimilar. The Christian starts from faith, and reaches a certain experience, in divine charity, of the God of Revelation, experiencing "Emmanuel", God with us, God with me. The Hindu has only empirical data to guide him and at the end of his road discovers a sublime but almost savage isolation.

It should not be a matter for surprise that one technique

should be common to both, when such different pursuits and paths are followed. Men in all places are men, and to reach a higher aim, to live according to the spirit—in whatever sense this may be understood—they have to get over the same obstacles, face the same difficulties and avoid the same snares. All these are put in the way of a deep inner life by the necessity of living and also by the fact that man has to try to bring a discord which may be overt or latent into harmony with his body, and even more with his rational thinking soul, and to restore the standing of spiritual values that have become thoroughly depreciated—all this in a human complex where disorder has broken in.[1]

The Hindu does not believe in sin (at least in sin as I view it by the light of faith). He is none the less marked by sin and by all the tares which were made the lot of man by the Fall. Like St Paul, he feels in his limbs the operation of a certain law which thwarts the aspirations of his soul. But to fight and win he does not have the grace of God through our Lord Jesus Christ (Rom. 7.22–5). To silence his senses, to bring to an end the digressions of a mind too sure of itself, and to liberate the spirit in him, he has nothing but human means. (This does not mean, however, that divine intervention, quite outside the laws and forms of Christian dispensation, a special aid from on high, might not come to his assistance.) I have the immense advantage over him of being a Christian, and therefore of being certain of seeing my efforts reinforced by grace and by our Lord Jesus Christ. But nothing stops me from making use of his purely empirical methods, and turning his technique to account in the conduct of my Christian life in order to fit myself for divine contemplation, for example, or to open myself to the action of the Spirit. Help yourself and heaven will help you. Nothing could be simpler; nothing could be wiser.

[1] See above, p. 69.

THE PRACTICE OF MEDITATION: BEING
FIRMLY SEATED

In a corner of your room place a fairly large cushion, say thirty inches by twenty, preferably thick but not soft—more a kind of hassock, stuffed with horsehair. Sit down on it and fold your legs as indicated in the posture of Reintegration

"THE PERFECT POSTURE"

(p. 95). Take up the Perfect posture, which is the most convenient: the *left* heel is driven well into the right groin, or set under the perineum, while the *right* foot rests on the left calf, with the heel firmly pressed against the abdominal wall. Later you will be able to assume the Hero posture: the left heel is placed as already described, but the right foot is now *on the left thigh*. You may even manage the Lotus posture, where the left foot is on the right thigh and the right foot on the left thigh. For a European this is clearly a feat. But it can be done by dint of regularly practising the Hero posture, and even the Perfect posture.

Once the legs are folded, the upper part of the body must be straightened without the knees leaving the floor. If need be, put a small cushion under the buttocks, or lean the base of the spine against the wall. Lift up the head so that the centre of gravity passes through the middle of the body—cranium, perineum, heels. Join the hands in front of the chest, or better still, place them palms up on the knees.

For the first months your joints will not stand up well to the twisting they are being given. It is better not to maintain this seated position for more than five minutes during the initial weeks. Break off and take up the posture of rest: lean your back against the wall, put the knees together and bring them up to the chin, pull the feet in against the body and the calves against the thighs; it is in fact the Folded Leaf (p. 93), but seated. Put the arms right round the legs and rest the head on the knees. You will soon feel the good that this seated, or rather crouching, posture does you. After a few minutes you can try the Perfect posture again. Or instead you may do one or other of the exercises recommended in connection with the posture of Reintegration.

Put energy, patience and optimism into all this. One fine day you will be rewarded, amply, for all your efforts. You will manage to maintain the Perfect posture for three, then five, then ten minutes. You will end up by assuming this posture effortlessly. The muscles and joints will no longer hurt, neither during nor after. As soon as you have taken up the posture, you will feel your body relaxing and a feeling of general well-being will establish itself in you. However curious it may appear, this mode of sitting or of crouching is "natural"; it gives you a feeling of balance, of being firmly seated, which affects the whole psychical being. To the absolute motionlessness of the body—which is almost impossible to maintain in the normal manner of sitting—there corresponds a surprising calm in the soul. The spirit has less trouble in focusing and concentrating its attention on someone or something. It is, effectively, an attitude of recollectedness.

CONCENTRATING THE MIND

Since they are subordinated to prayer, the classical Yoga postures, and especially the Perfect posture, must turn themselves into prayers. The suffering caused by the bruising of the joints, for instance, must not be without point. The spirit accepts this suffering, this "torture" inflicted on the body. The suffering acts as a springboard for the spirit, which at the same time gives it a meaning by introducing it into an ascetic discipline. The union or "joining" of body and soul must be compacted from this stage on. In our spirit, feelings of grief and compunction, the realization of our own indigence, and wretchedness, a state of self-abandonment and faith should consistently echo the trials imposed on our body.

It is a kind of purgative life, and may last several months. It gave me the opportunity of understanding and appreciating better my position as a Christian, a poor creature, yet with riches heaped on me; poor in myself, but rich in all the treasures of faith, hope and charity, offering themselves to me in Christ. I became aware, as I recited—slowly—the *Pater*, the *Credo* or even the *Confiteor*, of my self in relation to God. I rediscovered the dialogue God-me (*Ego hodie genui te*) and me-God (*Abba-Pater*). But the bruising of my joints and the need to move my body drove away true concentration and prevented the repose of my being in God.

I should in fact have been very willing to prolong this stage. But a new phase began for me the day my body became supple and my joints stopped complaining. I was able to remain still for a considerable time, and I experienced the recollections that belongs to Yoga and its practices. My mind became suddenly silent; my spirit attached itself to an idea, to one word only. I felt collected, focused on something. Nothing moved any more. *Animus* in me was as still as my body. My gaze, which had been fixed on my joined hands, lost itself in space. My breathing was slow and deep, exhalation almost imperceptible.

On another occasion, while in this calm of the senses, and silence of the mind, I was surprised to find myself repeating the name of Jesus the Saviour, in rhythm with the heartbeats I could feel. I had long known this very ancient practice which narratives, coupled with research and textual publications, have in recent years brought back into favour, and even perhaps popularized.[2] But I had had no suspicion of the depth of its significance, nor had I been able to see its practical application.

This privileged state of passive concentration lasted in my case for some weeks. Then, one day, faced with distractions and wanderings in my soul, I had to take up again exercises that till then had occupied me very little indeed, and initiate myself in the practice of active concentration.

THE PHASES OF SILENT MEDITATION

It will presumably be in this way that you will yourself begin your pilgrimage. Once you are properly seated and still, the trunk straight, carry out some *prāṇāyāmas*—unless your meditation follows the postures and the exercise recommended earlier on pp. 95–6. Your breathing must be calm, steady and silent.

[2] Cf. *La prière de Jesus*, by a Monk of the Eastern Church, Chevetogne, 1951; *Petite Philocalie de la prière du coeur*, translated into French and arranged by J. Gouillard, Cahiers du Sud, Paris, 1953.

Then put your whole being into a kind of *invocation* to the Lord, to the Living God. Repeat in your mind, as you breathe in or breathe out, or in time with the beating of your heart, a phrase you have chosen: "Father of all, to whom we go", "God our Saviour, God our Love", "God of my heart and of my understanding", "*Sanctus, sanctus, sanctus*", "God, Peace, *Śānti,* Joy". This formula must be a cry of faith, as well as a supplication, into which your whole being is poured. Do not worry in the least about anything irrational that it may appear to have about it. It will take you some time to find the ejaculatory prayer that suits you, that really takes hold of you, the prayer which, when meditation is over, remains at the heart of your being, and which you find joy in rediscovering, and hearing and saying again.

After some minutes you will pass on to the second stage in your meditation—a period of *gazing.*

Steady your eyes and "concentrate" them. Look fixedly straight ahead of you at a white curtain or a picture hanging on the wall (provided it is simple and beautiful), an inscription or a crucifix. Or else lower your eyes and look at your hands, left placed on right, between the knees. The ancients used to advise one strongly to look at a point of the body, just above the heart. In connection with this, interesting points are to be found in the *Philocalie du coeur* and in Blomm.[3] The essential point is that there should be no movement, or as little as possible. Keeping one's gaze quite still and focused on one point makes for concentrated and coherent thought.

Thought must at this point be fixed on something, on the object of the meditation, and remain poised there. This object may either come of its own accord, or may have been previously prepared or placed by you the evening before. It is not a question of analysing it nor of drawing ennobling

[3] A. Blomm, "L'Hesychasme, Yoga chrétien?" in *Yoga, science de l'homme intégral,* Cahiers du Sud, Paris, 1953, pp. 135-51.

considerations from it one by one, but simply of *seeing* it, *contemplating* it and the images it calls up in silence. Here is an example.

Today, Christmas Eve, I found in my missal, in the gradual of the Mass, these words taken from Scripture: "This night shall bring proof it was the Lord that rescued you from Egypt, and tomorrow you shall witness his glory. Give audience, thou that art the guide of Israel, that leadest Joseph with a shepherd's care. Thou who art enthroned above the Cherubim, reveal thyself to Ephraim, Benjamin and Manasses." Thereupon I *look* and *see* the Child who is to be born; I see him already in the arms of Mary, his mother. In this Child, I *contemplate*, without saying a word, him who comes from the bosom of his Father, where he rules over the choirs of angels, amongst us as Saviour. I stop, purely and simply to see this historical fact clearly and to let it sink in. Light, the true Light, predestined to lighten every man born on this earth, comes down to earth to live among us. This is the eternal Light, whence comes the halo that I see radiant about this child, "Shepherd of Israel", "Shepherd among us", yet at the same time "King of the Cherubim". I gaze; nothing more. Pictures, ideas (associations of ideas: Saviour—King—Light—Halo—Shepherd—Child—Light again) come one after the other, march past, if I may put it that way. I see them; I do not classify them, I do not make a tableau of them or an edifying sequence of reflections. And yet all these pieces of a sacred puzzle taken together arouse one idea in me; more than an idea, a silent vision of the whole mystery of Christmas.

This gives some insight into the method. But it will clearly be difficult for the uninitiated and even more for the person who practises discursive meditation to realize what it is about. It is also obvious that in silent meditation the gaze will be all the more penetrating, the images the more numerous and the vision of the whole all the richer according to the degree to which my mind is nourished by holy writ or by theology. The method of silent meditation is not a piece of learned ignorance. It presupposes that I am rich in Truth and in truths. But if it inherits at the same time a whole treasure-chest of preparatory acquisitions, it is content, unlike discursive meditation, to welcome what presents itself; it watches its object live, it does not work on it. Not analysis but synthesis.

Here are some easier examples which will be of help in understanding this.

I am thinking of the pericope of St John, which is read to us at the Mass of Maundy Thursday, and I gaze intensely, and without allowing myself to be distracted, at Christ as he is kneeling before his Apostles to wash their feet. I fix this image firmly in my mind. It naturally tells me a great deal about our Saviour, his love, his deep humility, his simplicity, his gentleness. I simply listen, and let my heart absorb this image and what it says. This may last a long while; and all I have done is to open my eyes and contemplate in silence.

In front of me there is a lighted candle. I observe it closely. In the very heart of the flame, there is a dark patch. An idea at once strikes me: "The hot and luminous part of the flame is our divine Saviour, manifesting the invisible and inaccessible Godhead. But for all that it is visible and hot, the flame itself—Christ—God—defies all analysis."

During the first days of Advent, I repeat as an invocation the liturgical phrase: "*Veni, Domine*—Come, O Lord!" And I hear, as if in reply: "Come and follow me"—echoing the gospel of the feast of St Andrew, which falls at about this time. My thought clamps on this double image of *veni*, and without making my intelligence do a stroke of work, without exerting my mind, I come to understand a great deal.

Countless themes for meditations of this kind can be found by laymen in the Bible and in the missal, and by priests and religious in the breviary. Beginners who find these themes too learned would be well advised to keep to the Our Father, the Creed and the Hail Mary. They should recite these prayers slowly, and stop at some idea or some word without trying to do any more than see properly—but giving themselves entirely to this seeing—what the idea or word expresses. The habit will soon form.

It is helpful to concentrate occasionally on objects apparently foreign to your personal religious life. For instance, you focus on one of these so-called current problems about which the consciences of so many people get worked up: an aspect of the social question that is near at hand, the loss of the sense of God amongst the masses, egoism at the heart of the nations, the sorry plight of such great numbers of oppressed people, the physical and moral misery of certain milieux. You will see in procession a crowd of poor people, of destitute people, of people persecuted in the name of justice. You will see, you will look—nothing more. This will be an excellent way of putting into practice the *Communicantes* of the Mass, a way of preparing yourself for the action of charity that is more efficacious and effective in many cases than the cold consideration of the means in our power of relieving misery and remedying evil.

It would of course be possible to concentrate on oneself. But here one must be governed strictly by prudence. The only way open to the Christian to fulfil himself is by seeing himself at the heart of the plan of redemption as a child of God, a sinner saved, a temple of the Spirit. We are only interested in that which, in us, interests our Father in heaven —our poverty and weakness, and our capacity to be and to live in him and by him. As for our sinful state, this need only hold our attention in meditation insofar as it urges us to throw ourselves into the arms of Christ in the course of meditation. We should not look on our weaknesses and culpable inclinations except in order to ask God to deliver us from them, if he so pleases. We should never concentrate on evil, sin or what can be an occasion of sin.

Here, finally, is a practice that I recommend to everyone. It is not a meditation in the proper sense of the term, but it provides a wonderful illustration of the method of silent meditation I have been describing, and it gives some hints as to the results.

Take as your theme these words of a psalm, well known to anyone familiar with the breviary:

"Would you but listen to his voice today!"
"Do not harden your hearts. . . ."

Repeat them, the first line as you breathe in, the second as you breathe out. Then in your mind run through the day ahead of you from waking in the morning to going to bed at night. *Look at* the different occupations of the day (everything you foresee) and *see* them linked as if *in a sequence, as a series of oblations you will make to the Lord.* Let them from that moment become for you the way in which you are called to live that very day, that *hodie,* as a child of your heavenly Father, fraternally with your brother-members of Christ, as a devoted and loving servant of your equals, your superiors and subordinates. Look well and foresee calmly everything that will be asked of you in generosity, devotedness and so on. See the places where your minutes or hours of prayer, your religious exercises, your work, your very moments of relaxation, will occur. This procedure will subtly bring about a certain adjustment. Look at all this steadily and at once throw yourself heart and soul into it all—"wish for and welcome absolutely everything that may happen to you". Let whatever is unforeseen and whatever cannot be foreseen be there already; or rather let your heart be ready (*Paratum cor meum, Deus, paratum cor meum*) to welcome what comes from the hand of God. I do not say to you: Make a plan, draw up a programme, think out how you will settle some matter. On the contrary, I say: Isolate yourself, concentrate yourself passively on the thought of what you will do. Open your innermost self to this known and unknown day. Go out towards it, and offer yourself to everything that it may bring. In this there is no scheming, but simply looking. After practising this kind of exercise a few times, you will, I think, be astounded to find that everything is getting along better, is working out, that your soul and spirit have less difficulty in bowing to circumstances. Much more than this, your faculties of intelligence and will will apply themselves positively and yet subconsciously to "problems" which you have rapidly taken in during your sweep of the horizon in meditation and set aside for what they are worth. At a given moment, you will find the solution ready to hand.

The *contemplative* phase in daily meditation may last ten or fifteen minutes, but its duration in fact varies a great deal, and how long it lasts is, moreover, of relatively little importance. This phase is followed by a shorter or longer period of silence, or perhaps we should say of greater silence, in which you no longer think of seeing anything, but all the more of assimilating, of uniting yourself, of thanksgiving. This is the ultimate phase. A void is made, and to fill it there comes, more taciturn than ever, the idea of God, the divine presence. Giving a final invocation, you say, "Until next time" to the Perfect posture. (But do not hesitate to take it up again if the opportunity arises; all you need do is take off your shoes.) You then turn back into the world of men, more man yourself, more convinced, and firmer too, about your duties as a Christian.

To be sure, I do not promise you, every day and on every occasion, a feeling of plenitude. There will be very arid days where you will be like a beast of burden and will be able neither to look nor to see; you will even find difficulty in keeping still. Do not worry; this is normal. But do not give up on any account. Nothing is won without difficulty. I may say that after four or five months of efforts and perseverance, I felt I was making no headway; but since then there have been few days when I did not feel the benefit of the exercises and especially of the practice of silent meditation.

V

FOR A CHRISTIAN YOGA:
PRACTICAL ADVICE AND GUIDANCE

THE AIM OF THE CHRISTIAN YOGI

"THE most recent data on matter and energy, and the latest discoveries in the field of psycho-physiology have notably brought together the frontiers of matter and spirit, and, while upholding the essential irreducibility of these two elements, they make it easier for us to understand their mysterious union in man, the microcosm and perfect synthesis of creation.

"It is the soul which, starting from the microscopic cell that acts as its support, builds up the body in accordance with the laws of biological evolution, and builds it up in its own image and likeness. These harmonious relationships between body and soul have been admirably brought to light by Father Gratry in a work that still has bearing today, *De la connaissance de l'âme*, by Father Poncel in his *Plaidoyer pour le corps*, Dr. René Biot, Dr. Carton in his numerous works, and Dr. Alexis Carrel. A struggle, in the proper sense, can never exist between these two elements, for there is in them nothing mutually contradictory; on the contrary, it is rather that the soul, the superior element, forms, educates and directs, while the inferior part, the body, is docile and collaborates. . . .

"Psycho-physiological laws have taught us that the body over which the spirit succeeds in exercising its mastery is healthier, stronger and calmer than the body, which the soul, abdicating its authority, leaves to the mercy of itself and its instincts. Then it moves rapidly downhill into ruin and decay, dragging the soul along to its fall. The law of the body resides in the spirit.

"Some writers on asceticism, whose spirit is imbued with the assumed antagonism between body and soul—the outcome of Cartesian and Jansenist dualism—treat the great task of personal sanctification as something frightening, a pitiless struggle between flesh and spirit, demanding dreadful austerities to which only exceptionally gifted beings could submit themselves. The spreading of these ideas in certain Catholic circles has diverted from sanctity some souls who would have reached that condition had they followed an ascetic discipline better adapted to human nature and to the laws of human activity. . . .

"We know well enough that original sin has made it more difficult for the spirit to govern the body; hence the need for vigilance. But it is a psychological error fraught with serious consequences to claim there is no other way to reach sanctity than by bullying and despising the body, by wishing to disregard or by violating the laws of healthy living, and by refusing to bestow respect, dignity and affection on our servant flesh.

"Can it be thought that a struggle to the death will enable the soul to establish control over the body? On the contrary, it is by forming and educating it wisely, not brutally, that the soul will spiritualize the body and raise it towards God. This spiritualization of the body will be much more easily reached by taking the peaceful and calm though energetic path of the Christian athletic ideal, than by the repulsive and painful method of a fight without issue and contrary to the very nature of our human life. Only a lofty bodily ideal is able, by its beauty and greatness, to cause the necessary enthusiasm to spring from the depths of the soul for the body to find health, strength, beauty, delight in living, spiritualization and ascent towards God in the restrictions placed on it and the efforts demanded of it and to accept them with alacrity and joy. The body, too, is made to love and glorify God, to take pleasure in him, and to have its share of the blessed state man will enjoy in the contemplation and love of the divine Being.

"The key to the whole affair can be summed up in this precept: sanctify the body by exercising it, work for the health and spiritualization of all its activities. Then, instead of being an obstacle to sanctity, the body will become an instrument."[1]

I have opened this chapter by quoting a passage written by a professor of physical education, who has a doctorate in philosophy. It supports the doctrinal and theological viewpoint set out earlier in this book.[2] Moreover, it underlines one of the aspects or goals of the Yoga programme set forth in this chapter. In his book, M. Marin traces the rules and defines the spirit of a Christian form of athletics, that is to say, of a sport or physical culture directed towards the development of the Christian in man. Our form of Yoga, by which I mean a whole collection of means and methods inspired by Yoga, is also orientated towards the Christian life. It aims similarly at making the body an instrument of sanctity, of prayer, and particularly of contemplative prayer. But it likewise postulates an attitude of respect for the human body and a healthy understanding of the relationship between flesh and soul.

It also insists on strength of will and an ascetic discipline; this is highly important. You cannot become a yogi, and especially not a Christian yogi, in a few days or months, any more than you can become an athlete in that time.

[1] Max Marin, l'*Athlète chrétien, Comment le former*, Presses de Belgique, Brussels, 1944, pp. 13–20.
[2] See above pp. 80–82.

Everyone must patiently undergo this period of apprenticeship and then practise and persevere for a long stretch of time.
A training programme is set out below in as great detail as
possible. In it, points will frequently be taken up that have
already been made in previous chapters. There will be greater
insistence on the spirit which must infuse the carrying out
of these exercises. Only one thing matters, and that is the
goal, the aim; it will come out more clearly in the following
pages.

THE BEGINNINGS OR THE PERIOD OF APPRENTICESHIP

Take courage. Strengthen your will. The early stages are not
hard, but they may be deceptive. A young man who is keen
on sport and used to the rapid movements of normal gymnastics, will perhaps not find it easy to keep himself to the
slow rhythm described on p. 36. A man of advanced middle
age who tries to carry out the Deep Obeisance, for instance,
will be shocked at not being able to touch the floor. He will
even get the feeling—which is frequently mistaken—that
he will never reach it. Everyone needs reminding that success
counts for much less than effort; the initial imperfections
and failures are stages on the way to success.

A. First learn to breathe

This is where you must begin. I shall not here again run
through what has already been said about the phenomenon of
breathing, about masculine and feminine patterns, about the
way of getting used to this admittedly subtle, but nevertheless important art of breath-control (pp. 110–112 above).
The Yoga apprentice must first learn to breathe without
assuming any postures. He must then train himself in com-
bining breathing with *āsanas*, beginning with the simplest.

The apprentice, let us say, is lying down in the posture of

Relaxation (pp. 101-103). If he is a man, he draws in his abdomen, emptying his lungs, as if the wall of the stomach had to touch the spine. On breathing in, he performs the inverse action; the stomach must be firm. Alternatively he may perform what is called "root contraction", where the diaphragm is first raised, and then lowered as far as possible (see pp. 39-40). During inhalation two hard masses must form on either side of the belly; they relax gently as he breathes out.

If the apprentice is a woman, she must inflate the chest and try to pull in the stomach as far as possible and raise the diaphragm. Instead of lying flat, she may first kneel, keeping the trunk erect, the shins against the floor and feet pointing backwards, and then sit back in a natural way on her heels, which are held together—this is the posture used by Carmelites. With hands placed on thighs, she may then take several slow breaths in this restful position.

A man may also take up the Folded Leaf posture (pp. 93-4) and practise drawing in the abdomen. This exercise, which is a little more difficult, marks a stage on the way to the perfect combination of postures and breathing.

B. The first training cycle

Even if a man or woman did not go beyond the stage just outlined, he or she would already be doing Yoga, a gymnastic without motion. Proper breathing is so important a thing that he would already be able to reap considerable benefits, provided of course that he carried out these exercises for a reasonable length of time, spending at least seven minutes morning and evening, apart from doing them on several other occasions during the day. Now we begin a second stage, comprising four or five postures that may properly be considered as belonging to Yoga.

Always begin by carrying out some breathing exercises,

standing with hands on hips. Take five or six complete abdominal or thoracic breaths, for instance, making equal pauses with full and empty lungs. Before beginning the exercise, you should have taken your pulse, and now you count silently five for each phase of the breathing cycle; or five for inhalation, three for the full-lung pause, five for exhalation and three with empty lungs. All sorts of rhythm combinations are possible. The essential point is not to wear yourself out, for this set of breathing exercises is meant to prepare you for the postures.

Now carry out the following *āsanas*:

1. *The Snake*. To lie down flat on your stomach, keep to the method given (p. 89). Once you are down, with the chest resting firmly on the backs of the hands, breathe easily and wait for a feeling of complete calm to spread through you; your heart must be beating gently and steadily. Then take up the position given (No. 3, p. 89), taking care that the hips remain as close as possible to the floor. The abdomen must be stretched. At first you should not stay longer than a second upon your arms. When you return to your starting position, carry on with your breathing exercises. Carry out the twofold action in this posture three times, making them progressively slower each time.

2. *The Dolphin* (No. 5, p. 91). This is the next exercise, and is intended for relaxation. It promotes intestinal massage by lowering the diaphragm to the limit.

3. *The Folded Leaf* (No. 7, p. 93) comes next, followed by *The Backstretch* (No. 8, p. 94). It should be noted that the main point in the latter posture is not to get the head on the knees, but to bend the back thoroughly and stretch the back muscles. You must therefore raise the arms, as already indicated, as high as you can; then stretch them out and ahead as far as possible as you lean forwards. Your hands should reach out beyond your toes. The difficult points are

keeping the knees from bending and keeping your breath. . . .
To begin with, take one breath only in this position. It will
be powerful and almost violent if you have taken care to
empty your lungs thoroughly as you leant forwards. With
time you will be able to hold this posture longer and take
five or six breaths. You will also assume it properly, with
head against knees and forearms along the shins. But patience
is necessary.

4. End this cycle with the posture of *Relaxation* (No. 13,
p. 102). After the considerable effort entailed in the Backstretch, relaxation will come all the easier and you will
scarcely need to order your muscles to slacken.

These five simple exercises arranged in an easy series already
act powerfully on the muscles and the internal secretion
glands. The Snake works the chest and abdominal muscles,
and also organs such as the liver, the spleen, the kidneys
(the suprarenal glands), and the thyroid gland. It acts so
strongly on the thymus that a few sessions will calm down the
most "choleric" persons. The Backstretch melts abdominal
fat and slims the hips. It tones up the prostate gland and the
spinal cord.

The best time to carry out the first session of these exercises
is on getting out of bed; if this is not possible, do it a little
later, but before breaking your fast. An excellent time for a
second session is in the evening before supper. On each
occasion the exercises should be carried out either in the
open air or with the windows open and as lightly dressed
as possible.

C. *The second cycle*

I do not imagine that any discomfort could be felt in
carrying out these five initial postures. After a fortnight you
will have got used to them. You may then add No. 1, the
Deep Obeisance, provided you do not expect to take up the

correct pose at the first attempt, and provided you do not try to remain in this posture. Do the whole thing in one breath to begin with, drawing the abdomen in and breathing out as you bend down, and breathing in and relaxing as you straighten up. Then try to take one or two complete breaths in the forwards-bent position, with the hands touching the floor or close to it. Try too to place your forearms along your shins and to grasp your ankles (see variant on No. 1, p. 86).

The Deep Obeisance may be done thrice, each time making prayer specially chosen or composed for the occasion (this will be explained further on).

You may also add No. 2, the Tree (p. 86), and finally No. 10 the Candle, and No. 11, the Plough (pp. 96–8). The Plough fits in best between the Backstretch, No. 8, and the posture of Relaxation, No. 13; or between the Folded Leaf, No. 7, and the Backstretch. You will not remain in the Plough posture for more than three or four complete breath-cycles, but you may carry out the Candle twice or even thrice to become familiar with these linked postures, and especially to get used to passing from one into the other smoothly and slowly, keeping the legs straight and stiff. It should be noted that these two postures give a feeling of complete relaxation, and freedom. By acting on the heart and the spinal marrow, they stimulate the functions of the intellect, such as the memory. After a siesta, doing the Candle posture restores you completely to waking existence.

Here then is an excellent little series that takes ten minutes or at most a quarter of an hour; the Deep Obeisance (thrice), the Snake (thrice), the Folded Leaf, the Plough and the Candle (thrice each), the Backstretch, and finally the posture of Relaxation. The sense of well-being that follows it makes you look forward to it from first thing in the morning; and you will not let slip the opportunity of doing it again in the evening, or, if need be, before going to bed.

D. *The third cycle*

You will soon be able to run right through from No. 1 to No. 11, in the order given earlier in this book for standing and sitting postures, and always finishing up with the addition of No. 13. If any posture wearies you or demands excessive effort, drop it. If you find your heart beating rather strongly after any posture, the effort made has been too great; you should then remain longer in the succeeding posture of ease, or if necessary take up the posture of Relaxation itself.

You must not under any circumstances begin the Pole, No. 12, until your body has become really supple, and you feel thoroughly at your ease with the exercises and already under the power of yogic discipline. This posture will call for long and patient effort on your part. If need be, carry it out separately from the others. Leave it until bedtime for instance, and do it on your bed. Before you begin, the heart should be calm and the nerves relaxed. You must exercise caution; and in particular you may only increase the time of remaining in this posture slowly and gradually, beginning with a few seconds and working up gently to one minute and then to two. Yet it has an almost radical effect on brain fatigue; it cures headaches. . . . But it only becomes effectively relaxing after a considerable period of practice, the length of which varies from person to person.

E. *Combining breathing, postures and prayer*

It should naturally not be assumed that having the technique for the postures at the tips of your fingers, and being in complete control of your breathing, should enable you to set your efforts and practice moving clearly in the right direction. The "way of silence" is "a method of contemplation inspired by Yoga". As has already been said, it aims at making the body a good instrument for the contemplative life. It presupposes your having a particular intention; and it comprises a whole collection of means.

Amongst these means, there is what is called "breathed prayer". This has already been referred to (p. 127). It consists of repeating a selected phrase in one's mind as one breathes in and out. If possible this phrase should accentuate the symbolic import of human breathing, and serve as a channel through which man can wholly transmit himself through the medium of his breath. It can and even should marry itself to the rhythm of breathing; or rather it should form this rhythm. It helps the apprentice-yogi to breathe properly; and for the yogi, whose formation is complete, it is second nature.

Before beginning the exercises in the morning, I wash (taking care to wet myself from head to foot), I brush my teeth and drink several mouthfuls of water (which does not break my fast), and then stand facing the open window. Relaxed, smiling slightly and looking straight ahead without focusing on anything, I begin to breathe in, silently pronouncing this verse of Psalm 118:

> Rises ever a sigh from my lips,

and even, if my breathing rhythm is already slow enough:

> Rises ever a sigh from my lips,
> as I long after thy covenant.[3]

And I see this breath from God, that I am eager for, I feel it fill me and quicken my whole being. Not only is my blood purified in this wonderful exchange of which even the tiniest cells of my lungs bear witness; the innermost depths of my whole life as man and Christian are plumbed by it, my strength swells and my heart expands. Merely from paying attention to a phenomenon as everyday as this

[3] (The French goes: *J'ouvre la bouche et j'aspire,*
   J'aspire tou souffle, ô Seigneur.
   —TRANSLATOR.)

inhalation, I have been able to endow it suddenly with a hidden meaning. It is not only my body but my soul and spirit also that the breath of the Almighty comes to awaken and seize.

For a few moments I keep my lungs full, poised somehow in the wonder that is taking place in me. Then I gently exhale this "corrupted" air, saying silently (from Psalm 50):

> . . . my God, bring a clean heart to birth within me;
> breathe new life, true life, into my being.

I may repeat the same phrase five or ten times without wearying of it. It will form the rhythm of my breathing, and give it symbolic meaning. Tomorrow, very probably, a different prayer will accompany this munificent air in its "going-out and coming in". I might for instance recite in my mind some verses from the sequence of Pentecost which I, as a Christian yogi, love.[4]

An appealing call as you breathe in; then a pause, and a soothing expression as you breathe out. . . . It is for you to find the words that fit this pattern. "Jesus, Jesus. . . . Amen, Amen"; "Lord, O Lord. . . . *Fiat, Fiat*". In only a few days, once you are beyond the inevitable phase of groping, you will notice with surprise how easy this simple expedient makes deep breathing, and above all how it promotes spiritual *engagement*.

This breathed prayer must on no account disturb the course

---

[4] (The French translation of *Veni Sancte Spiritus* which follows is in two-line stanzas, beginning:

> Viens donc, Esprit-Saint
> O douce présence.
>
> Viens, Consolateur,
> Tendre Apaisement.

This is a considerable departure from the Latin. Moreover, it matches the English translation (by Mgr Knox) of this sequence so ill that it is useless to give of your apprenticeship in any way. Although prayer helps me to breathe, there are presumably some people, especially amongst the beginners, who find it too complicated to keep control over their breath and to make themselves say a prayer at the same time. Take one thing at a time. Each paragraph in this chapter marks a further step. No one should be in any way surprised if the transition from one stage to another should prove laborious. Do not force anything, and do not worry about any failure.

The next step after linking breathing to mental prayer is to do the same for the movements and postures.

As I bend forwards for the Deep Obeisance, for instance, I say "Our Father", and as I stand up again, "Thy Kingdom come". The second time I say, "God of God . . . Light of Light", and the third, "Holy Spirit . . . consuming Fire". Or on each occasion I say, "To the Lord of Ages, all honour and glory".

The Tree posture (to which I shall shortly be returning) lends itself admirably to ejaculatory prayer. As I lift my arms with my hands joined, I say, "All my heart goes out to thee, O Lord my God". And, standing motionless, I go on: "Belie not the trust I have in thee, let not my enemies boast of my downfall." "Direct my way, Lord, as thou wilt, teach me thy own paths." "O God my deliverer, my abiding hope." "Forget not, Lord, thy pity, thy mercies of long ago." "Give heed no more to the sins and frailties of my youth, but think mercifully of me, as thou, Lord, art ever gracious." "Uprightness and purity be my shield, as I wait patiently, Lord, for thy help." All these verses of Psalm 24 will emphasize the opening of the arms, the gestures of welcome or

the latter as an equivalent, especially as the French version fits the breathing pattern (first line, in; second line, out) while the English, like the Latin, is in three-line stanzas. An English translation of this French version would render the content, but would not constitute an aid to meditation.—Translator.)

offering and the attitude of abandonment which were set out in describing this posture (pp. 86–9). It will even occur, it will in fact necessarily occur, that the gesture speaks by itself. An advanced yogi will not need to compress into phrases the feelings in his heart. This method that I am recommending is therefore a step, and a big step, towards the silent prayer discussed earlier. Meanwhile the apprentice yogi will, I hope, experience the sweetness of this prayer that embraces the whole of man.

F. Really understanding what one is doing, and really wanting to do it

Now comes the next step. The apprentice yogi must gradually pay attention to the symbolic meaning of the postures he takes up. For him it is a matter of consciously entering into a kind of game and of thoroughly understanding what is going on, in order to be able to give himself to it.

Every posture, obviously enough, jogs our bodies in some way, by working a muscle, for instance, or by stimulating a gland. But each of them likewise acts on our psychical being and composes us in spirit. Take the Tree posture, which is one of those that provide a good illustration of the basic principle underlying our form of psychosomatic culture. It is a symbol that calls into being what it symbolizes. To put this in another way, the Tree posture is one of these exercises done with a purpose, in which I make my body assume an attitude that corresponds, in the way that a symbol corresponds to the real thing it represents, to the attitude I wish my soul and spirit to assume. I am restless or upset; ideas clash confusedly in my mind; or I am simply absent-minded, my thoughts wander, my imagination strays, my understanding steals away. I am thus in no condition to work or pray. But if I succeed in stabilizing my body, if I compel it to fight against instability and remain for some time in a balanced posture, I impose a degree of immobility on my soul at the same time. I tie it down by withdrawing its attention from everything that engrosses it, and by forcing it to pay attention to an action that would appear to have nothing to do with it, but which in fact does have considerable bearing.

In the Tree posture I find balance and stability, as well as uplift, for my whole being. I stand straight. My body makes the least possible contact with the ground, on which only the sole of one foot rests. My hands, joined, stretch upwards; so does my soul. However faintly a prayer such as "To thee, my God, do I lift up my soul" comes to my mind (and this will unfailingly happen, or, if not, I must call it up in the manner set out in the foregoing paragraph), my gesture or attitude will first suggest, or in some way provoke and then express, a springing up of my whole being towards God, towards heaven. During the day I shall only need to call to mind or carry out partially the gesture with joined hands to put my spirit again in touch with higher things.

All this goes to illustrate a phenomenon that plays, and must play, a considerable part in our lives: the repercussion of gesture and bodily attitude on the soul, and conversely the echoing by the body of the spirit's attitude. Those of us who are monks habitually omit deep bows from our prayer. This gesture is meant to express the feeling in our soul. What we actually do expresses our feeling all too truly. In watching a monastic choir today, you may see many bows poorly carried out; by and large, the attention paid to Divine Office is on the ebb. Liturgical prayer no longer grips us. Our souls wander here and there during the psalms. Our gestures and attitudes, performed anyhow, embody the "anyhow" of our spirit with regard to God. To force ourselves to take care over our gestures and to make sure they are done and done well—this very concern provides us with a way of reducing the tendency to roam. It is impossible for a genuflection properly done, where the knee actually touches the floor and does so gently, to fail to produce an echo in our soul. A real kneeling on the ground, maintained for some time, will express an inner attitude or will arouse it, call it forth. This, at least, may be verified by a merely moderate degree of attentiveness. I naturally disregard the smoothly performed gestures of all the hypocrites, the falsely devout, the Pharisees. Yet it should be remembered that actors while on the stage have been converted by "acting", by imitating the gestures and attitudes of certain saints. Without their realizing it, their souls, or rather the depths of their soul (*spiritus*), have been touched and then gripped by the action.

But to return to Yoga. Perhaps not all the postures described are able to call up or create an inner gesture or disposition of the soul. All nevertheless link the body to the soul and, beyond the resulting improvement in the psychosomatic condition, there is also this joining and interpenetration as a result of which my soul, relieved of all worries, cut off from the outer world, and having in addition thrust aside all rational activity, remains for a considerable time nothing more than a "form" of my body, whom its sole function is to sustain and sublimate.

Try to count the number of occasions in a day, or in an hour, when the body enjoys the presence of the soul, when the soul has given itself entirely to its life companion, when the activities of both are exactly in harmony. These moments are rare; they may even be non-existent. The same is true when both are working together; I am thinking of choral prayer, in which the *mens* is supposed to agree with the voice. Each goes it own way. The body is there, true enough, but is it really present at the chanting of the soul? And is not the soul for its part absent nine times out of ten, led away by its own trains of thought, carried off by memories far from the "place" where body and soul are supposed to be performing a task in common? This is but one example, a case of divorce in which great harm is done to the spirit, which would have benefited markedly from unity of body with soul.

The prevailing tenor of life together for the two of us, or rather the three of us (see pp. 63–70), is one of distraction, disjunction and even rupture.

The exercises of Yoga are meant to remedy this ill, to re-educate body and soul, to show them again how to agree and live truly in each other. To do this the exercises use a fundamentally simple and modest instrument. Yet this modesty is a factor in its success. I am alone, quite withdrawn into the silence and privacy of my room. I am lightly dressed or even naked. Then, by trying to perform a series of postures of varying degrees of difficulty and complexity as well as I can, though without straining my spirit, I oblige my soul to give itself over entirely to my body, to the movements of which it must pay attention. I go beyond merely arousing its interest in the correct performance of some acrobatics; I invite it to marry, consciously, the attitudes of my body and to let itself be influenced by them. My soul is in action, since my will directs the carrying out of the exercises, and since my intelligence watches over the quality of the performance. But at the same time my soul is passive, for it is cut off from outside influences and from its own memories, worries and preoccupations and is therefore only able at this time to benefit to the full from a whole series of phenomena manifested in the body, such as the improved circulation of the blood, the decongestion of certain organs, the toning up of nerves and muscles and brain, the clearing of the respiratory canals and lungs, greater equilibrium between the humours, the stimulation of internal secretion glands, and so on. All this is of interest to, and acts on, the soul. It is all a factor in "animal *and* spiritual" life.

How pleasantly relaxing the Pole posture becomes for the person who has had the strength of will to get used to it! It is the most striking of all Yoga postures, as well as the posture the correct assumption of which calls for the greatest assiduity and perseverance. It demands character and energy, for you have to conquer yourself and your fears, to succeed at it. It is therefore highly formative. But that is not all. At the same time as it rests the heart, which now beats very much more easily, and dispels fatigue by flushing out the brain, it frees you from two apparently opposite complexes. It gradually eliminates emotional anxiety and equips man with a perfect understanding of his own balance. The feet are in the air, the body is stretched but not stiff; in fact it is relaxed, and this upside-down position is the most restful of them all. You are straight and still; you feel yourself, in command of yourself. You are filled with calm self-assurance; and this spells the end of that painful inferiority complex for all timid and inhibited people. Conversely it marks the beginning of modesty for the proud and cocksure. To stand on your head implies defying ridicule. The posture is humble, and makes for humility. It sets man up at heaven but in a way quite incompatible with any haughty pride. It is a sign; a symbol that brings about what it symbolizes. Whoever thinks he is wise enough may try to explain this— if he can, for in this context the relations between physical and spiritual remain deeply mysterious.

It must in fact be clear to everyone that the spiritual life will be affected by exercises in which body and soul are in possession of each other and work together, for and in each other. As the various and complex elements in man become joined, so does that which in each of us constitutes man unfold and expand; this may be happening unconsciously, but it is all the surer for that.

Must I excuse myself for this apparent digression? To me

it seems to be of capital importance in instructing and forming a yogi-to-be, that his attention should be drawn by the
use of concrete examples to the meaning and significance
of the exercises he is to do, right from the start.

I am now going to assume he is in command of his art, or
at least that he is able to carry out the complete series of
postures without any trouble or strain. I shall also take it that
he has realized the phenomenon just set out, and is accustomed to relate attitudes as well as breathing to prayer. It
remains for me to map out an initial daily programme.

THE DAY OF THE CHRISTIAN YOGI

The day of a Christian yogi must be, as it were, under the
aegis of two series of exercises or postures, two sessions
differing in character and significance: a session of *engagement*
in the morning (or of readjustment, if it is put off till a little
later), and a session of *relaxation* in the evening.

A first pattern

I recommend this one for beginners. The morning session,
after some exercises in abdominal, thoracic or complete
breathing (see pp. 110–12), should consist of the following
postures:

1. *The Deep Obeisance* (No. 1). To be held for a short
   while; enough, say, for four deep breaths.
2. *The Tree* (No. 2). In this very important posture the
   yogi should remain for several minutes. He should
   combine it, as said above, with the postures of welcome,
   elevation, abandonment and offering. He must make
   sure that it is a prayer.
3. *The Snake* (No. 3). To be done thrice, with four rests
   (chest on backs of hands, and lying flat on the ground);
   one rest before the lifts begin and one after each lift.
4. *The Bent Bow* (No. 4). Also three times, with three

pulls and three subsequent rests. Breathe in as you bend; hold your breath when bent; breathe out as you unbend.

5. *The Dolphin* (No. 5). To be held long enough for four to six abdominal breaths.

6. *The Candle* (No. 10), together with *the Plough* (No. 11). Thrice, taking at least four breaths each time.

7. *The Backstretch* (No. 8). Four deep breaths.

8. *The posture of Relaxation* (No. 13). Twelve complete breaths, drawing the stomach well in on each exhalation. Or else carry out a few *prāṇāyāmas* (see pp. 112–14).

This session should be done before breakfast, and preferably immediately after washing or taking a shower. If you feel too stiff then, just do the Tree and postpone the rest until, say, before the midday meal. At all events, have no hesitation about "losing" fifteen, twenty or thirty minutes of the morning, the earlier the better, in *engagement* or re-adjustment; you will be handsomely repaid for it.

The evening session will consist of:

1. *The Pole* (No. 12). Take up to twenty deep but gentle breaths. Breathe in through the nose, out through the mouth with the lips only slightly apart, as slowly as you possibly can.

2. *The Full Backwards Bend* (No. 6). As for the Pole. This posture, which at the outset is very exacting, must have become comfortable. Stretch up your arms beyond your head so that they continue the line made by your trunk. This will make your chest expand and deepen your breathing. Alternatively you may place your arms along your body at the sides. At the end of the posture the arms must be completely relaxed and feel heavy, as if stuck to the ground. On being raised, they should fall heavily back. This experience should help you to relax; do it several times, especially in the earlier stages.

3. *The Folded Leaf* (No. 7). Remain in this posture until you feel completely calm and relaxed.

These three postures may take you some ten minutes. End up with the Carmelite posture, kneeling and sitting back on your heels; or try to assume the posture of Reintegration (p. 95). If you are already used to the Perfect posture, which you will certainly have attempted during the period of apprenticeship, take it up for a short while.

This second session should be carried out in the evening, either before the evening meal, or just before going to bed, provided sufficient time has gone by since eating. In any case, once you are in bed, you should carry out No. 13 again, which prepares you admirably for sleep.

A second pattern

This is meant for the more advanced. It involves switching the more difficult exercises to the morning session, by way of preparation for meditation. The series therefore runs as follows:

1. *The Pole.* This is done immediately after the introductory breathing exercises, and should last for as long as five or even ten minutes. It will flush out the brain, and produce complete relaxation and an overall feeling of calm—the first step towards effectively attaining a state of recollectedness.

2. *The Full Backwards Bend.* This *āsana* must likewise be kept up for some time. The attention should be focused on the solar plexus (which in practice comes to mean the pit of the stomach), where the pulsing of the arteries should be felt after a minute or two.

3. *The Folded Leaf.* These three postures alone should be allowed at least ten minutes. Then take up the Perfect, or better still the Hero posture, carry out a few *prāṇāyāmas*,

and begin meditation at once. (This will be dealt with
further on.)

The evening session consists of the whole series of postures
performed in the order already set out.

According to the pattern adopted, each of the two daily
sessions may take from fifteen to twenty-five minutes. That
is relatively little. Yet it is enough, for it is quality, not
quantity, that counts. At other times during the day, you
should take pains to keep intact your formation as a yogi.
I recommend the following points.

1. *Breathing*

Carry out exercises, not merely on the occasions that I have
described (pp. 111–12), but also at any loose moment. A full
series of *prāṇāyāmas* towards midday is excellent. First take
your pulse and use its rhythm: inhalation, three (or four)
beats; holding the breath, twelve (or sixteen) beats; exhalation, six (or eight) beats. Lengthen these phases only very
gradually and do not try to go beyond your limit. After
more than two years, my limit is still 6 : 24 : 12. Under these
conditions, the exercises are not dangerous in the least
(heart-cases are discussed at the end of this chapter). Beware
particularly of trying for the "minimum limit" of the
Indian yogi—12 : 48 : 24—which presupposes a long training.
This rhythm, moreover, seems to me not to help us towards
our goal of finding calm and establishing in ourselves a
silence conducive to pure prayer; we are not striving to
create in ourselves extraordinary psychological or parapsychological conditions.

One further piece of advice. As you breathe in, take care
to direct the air to the base of the lungs. You draw in the
abdomen. Imagine the life-force, or *prāṇa*, as the Indians say,
that flows into you with the air you inhale, descending to
the level of the perineum. As soon as you begin holding

your breath, start counting silently and at the same time imagine this life-force or *prāṇa* slowly moving upwards again. The abdominal pressure will at once lessen and the air will in fact mount towards the top of the lungs. As you breathe out, imagine the life-force escaping upwards out of your body. By following these instructions you will avoid one inconvenient factor about this exercise, which in fact only occurs rarely and with certain types of temperament, namely, the involuntary concentration on the lower organs and from this a possible stimulation or awakening of sexual desire. I say "possible" because in general it appears that the opposite effect is more frequently produced.

2. Carriage and bearing

Develop the habit of standing really erect. When you are standing, keep your weight on your heels, with your feet more or less at right angles. The arms hang naturally at the sides, palms facing forwards. Instead of throwing your weight first on one foot, then on the other, as you undoubtedly usually do without realizing the hip-twisting that this causes, keep your weight equally on both feet. Your heels should be either touching, or held not too far from each other at a distance you find suitable. The stylized posture of the Tree will have trained you for this. "He who is able to do the greater, can do the lesser. When one can stand straight on one foot, it is child's play to stand straight on two."[5]

Practise also sitting squarely, without making use of any support for your back. If you feel tired on coming back from a long outing, do not try to rest in an armchair. Stretch out on a rug on the floor and take up the posture of Relaxation. Alternatively, sit as I have said and place your hands, palms upwards, near the knees. Slacken the facial muscles, breathe

[5] P. Chanson, *Sacerdoce et célibat*, Ed. du Levain, Paris 1952, p. 83.

deeply, and after a few moments of immobility your weariness will have disappeared.

Whenever you can, walk in the Eastern fashion, shoulders back, muscles and palms facing out. "In this way you provide your whole body with a logical, rational equilibrium, and as you move on, you benefit from the rests and respites inherent in the vertical position with which we are endowed by providence."[6] "To begin with this gait seems more tiring than the normal way of walking. But a little training shows us that, on the contrary, it requires less energy."[7]

3. *The prayer of the heart*

In addition to breathed prayer and postured prayer, which were recommended earlier, here is another and subtler practice which will benefit you greatly.

Let a deep calm spread through you, and remain like this for some time. Instead of taking a dull siesta, for instance, stretch yourself out flat in order to relax as fully as possible. If possible you should be naked; if need be, throw a coverlet over yourself. Shut your eyes and breathe gently, keeping your hands on your chest, which should not rise and fall as you breathe, or, if it does, should do so almost imperceptibly. Listen to or rather feel your heart beating, but without straining your attention; you are inadvertently aware of the beating. At first your heart will beat rather fast—this is always true of the very earliest stages—but soon it will calm down and become like a voice or a light touch within you.

Give yourself up and yield to the influence of this rhythm. Then form a prayer, a leaping up of your whole being, for each heart-beat. Say silently, for instance: "My . . . God"—"My . . . Lord"—"Jesus . . . Jesus"—"Saviour . . . Saviour".

[6] P. Chanson, *op. cit.*, p. 106.

[7] P. Chanson, *Pour la santé du corps et de l'esprit*, Spes, Paris, 1955, p. 94.

You must find your own word or phrase, or rather your own invocation to provide a channel for your whole being to pass through, and which, linked to the organ which manifests life in you and from which it springs, becomes truly significant as a symbol.[8]

Gradually, evenly, you will reach a condition of true silence, which will, however, be the opposite of the void or emptiness usually called up by the word "silence". For it will consist of attentiveness, both active and passive, on the part of your whole being, and the opening of the heart of your life to adoration and love.

4. *A degree of asceticism*

This ideal that I have been setting out is not a matter to be taken lightly. The "way of silence" is the very opposite of a game. It presupposes a certain pattern of living, which need by no means be monastic, but does imply an ascetic discipline. Athletic training includes something of this; the method of Hébert is strict, hard and austere. In his works, M. Marin stresses the part played by temperance and chastity, to say nothing of character, in the ideal sought by the Christian athlete.

One would naturally expect no less from a Christian yogi-to-be. From the time he becomes an apprentice he will, moreover, feel the need for certain restraints, for practising a number of more difficult virtues and for carrying out disciplines that nature does not at first take to easily. He will respond to the hidden tendencies aroused in him by the postures, such as non-violence (see pp. 104–8). But his principal care will be to live up to the ideal of the Gospel and the Beatitudes, where a complete programme is to be found.

[8] The appendix contains some texts relating to this practice, which dates from the early centuries of the Church and of the monastic movement.

The discipline of the postures constitutes an asceticism in itself. It must fit naturally into the pattern and practice of Christian living, and become one with it. That is the mark of success. To accomplish this demands strength of will. Give yourself to it. Make a promise of steadfastness to God and to yourselves.

"Every athlete", says St Paul, "must keep all his appetites under control." We are familiar, too, with the kind of abstinence preached today not only by the handbooks of athletes and sport mentioned above, but also—quite apart from popular books on medicine—the techniques hawked out to everyone wishing to acquire or re-acquire shapeliness, beauty, strength, energy, and to develop on the purely human plane of mental and physical being. "Do not smoke, or only very little; drink good wine, in moderation. Forbid yourself spirits; never take liquor; above all none of those drinks that are claimed to stimulate the appetite or the digestion. Cut out from your diet all useless foodstuffs, such as spices, pepper, mushrooms, all kinds of condiment, sweets, cream pastry, cold meats. Eat instead only a little red meat, plenty of green vegetables and raw fruit." This ultra-monastic diet is, however, strongly recommended to laymen by a layman. It is also the diet for a yogi. I would add, do not eat unless you are hungry, nor drink unless you are thirsty. Eat to satisfy your hunger; but you must be able, if not always, at least occasionally, to leave the table hungry. Try to fast from time to time. After the morning session, when your body has been given plenty of air and light, it will require no more than a light breakfast. Do not for goodness' sake force it to take a full meal. Train yourself to do without things whenever need may arise; and now and then, say once a month, fast properly for a whole day, taking only bread and water.

Gradually, and using discretion, make your body resistant

to cold. The breathing exercises prescribed before each session are partly intended to warm you up when, for instance, in the depths of winter you dress scantily to carry out the postures. Granted, it takes courage to undress and bare one's body on a frosty day. If you are not strong and much affected by the weather, keep a woollen vest on. But I imagine that you will very soon be able to face any temperature happily.

I do not recommend an ice-cold or even a cold shower every morning. But become as familiar with water as you are with air. Wet the body from head to foot in the morning, just using a face-cloth, and in the evening too. When you can, and the weather permits, don't be afraid to go and take a dip in the river.

This somewhat revolutionary programme is really quite simple. Putting it into practice demands strength of will and character, admittedly. But you soon get into the way of it; and in this "life according to nature" that it comprises, "nature smiles at the things of nature".[9]

There is no apparent distinction between a Christian yogi and any other man. He belongs to his *milieu* and lives in it. He eschews on principle whatever might mark him out. Although a trained eye may be able to recognize him by his gait, bearing, gestures or reserve, he does not try to draw attention to himself in any way. He carries out his practices alone, with no onlookers. He does not discuss his exercises except with those who wish to follow him. On the other hand, he does not make a secret of them; yet they do form part of his private life, and are therefore covered by a veil of discretion.

On his own, and alone in himself, the Christian yogi is able to pay all the more attention to the effects his art and his

[9] William of Saint-Thierry, "Lettre d'or", from *op. cit.* on p. 63.

exercises are having on him and in him. He carefully notes
the natural and spontaneous tendencies discussed above,
which manifest themselves at all levels, physical, psychical and
spiritual. But he treats them as signs, and as means rather
than ends.

His ultimate goal is that of every Christian (if his life is in
the world), and of every member of a religious order (if he
is a monk). The difference lies merely in the fact that a
certain character is breathed into whatever expresses his life
as a Christian, or monk, or priest. He puts as it were a seal
on everything he does.

He goes even further; he wishes to improve on it. To do
so he puts his whole being into what he is doing. He shuns
routine automatism. He wishes to be recollected and in
control of his reflexes. He intends to be in complete command
of himself, so that he may truly carry out what is required of
him, and also so that he may welcome whatever occurs.
Mere habit detracts greatly from a man's merit. It debars
him from benefiting from the true and effective presence of
the agent in what he is carrying out; it prevents the *engagement* of the doer in the thing done; the living imprint left
by the heart on any word or action in which it has really
taken part and expressed itself.

We are too frequently and too easily absent from what we
are doing. Our attention is wanting; the purpose and meaning of it suffers; and what we have done leaves our hands
lacking in *soul*. It is still-born, an action without meaning, a
word with no life, through which neither heart nor spirit flows.

Improvement implies, in the first place, being there. The
Christian yogi wishes to make sure that he will be truly
present in what he is doing.

He reaches this goal by means that are kept simple and
humble so as to disconcert the profane, whence the discretion
recommended a few paragraphs above. The worldly person

will never see, or only very vaguely, the connection between the action of controlled breathing, when properly carried out, and the perfection of an ordinary action that is like any other. He will be bewildered at the possibility of a series of bodily postures influencing prayer, and exerting a real effect on a life of prayer, on union with God and love of one's neighbour. A smile, a joke, even a shrug of the shoulders. . . . He is so sure of *his* own means, and in particular so convinced of the irrelevance and purposelessness of the body with regard to things of the spirit and the spiritual life. . . .

Let him be. As a Christian yogi you know and feel in advance all that the spirit can expect from the body, from movements well performed. You are no longer at the initial stages and know from experience the influence that calm breathing has on your innermost life. Of your body—which is no enemy to you—you gradually make a faithful servant. You order it (and it obeys) to help you to practise fully even virtues as great as faith, hope and Christian charity. To go even better, you have discovered this means—I dare scarcely say this trick—of carrying out whatever you do with your whole being, of being one and united in order to act, of possessing yourself in order to give yourself, of being master in order to serve. There are many aims for our form of Yoga to accomplish.

The Christian yogi does better, and also does more. This is to some extent in consequence of having a special kind of health, bound over to the service of sanctity. Calmed, rested and relaxed as he is, why should he not be capable of more as well as of better?

He wishes to have greater faith and, in face of the mystery of God which he sees and looks at intensely, a keener understanding of his place as a Christian and as a child. His aim is to fix his life in hope, in a kind of anticipated beyond; he bases his happiness on the very idea of his salvation, and his

joy on the certainty of being raised by Christ and really taken
into the embrace of him who was crucified. He wishes to
open himself to charity, to love and to be loved; to give himself, and yield himself entirely to God in well-defined acts—
carrying out every day the will of heaven. He wishes to
enjoy God as far as he is able and to experience the love of
God in so far as this may be the will of the Holy Spirit.

The Christian yogi is ready for all sacrifices, he is positively
disposed to them—which does not mean that they cost him
nothing. He intentionally uses discretion, for instance in
mortification, but does so without any selfish motive; and in
work, as in prayer, he wishes to be open-hearted. He aims at
more, since his practices fit him for more. He has the advantage over others of feeling in better condition, which strikes
him as an invitation from God not to languish in the ghastly
mediocrity that so quickly satisfies your bourgeois, whether
layman, priest or monk.

The true Christian yogi always tends to find life too easy.
He questions himself and consults his Master: "What do
you think of this, Lord?" . . .

THE MEDITATION OF THE CHRISTIAN YOGI

It is in meditation and more particularly in the silent meditation discussed above (pp. 126–33) that the Christian yogi
becomes aware of his duties and patiently strives to set his
innermost life in harmony with God and the divine will.
Breathed prayer, postured prayer and prayers of the heart are
the preparation for yogic meditation, which is in turn linked
to postures that may be called postures of stabilization; of
these the Perfect and even more the Lotus posture are
characteristic examples. In the same way as the postures of
uplift, balance and union, they too call into being what they
symbolize; they create calm and bring about equanimity.
Like the other postures, they demand strength of will, but

to a higher degree. They can only be properly assumed and become really restful after conscientious, persevering and energetic practice. They hurt for a long time. Man has to gain command over his own body by strength of character and the ability to endure. It is true that in themselves, as postures of complete relaxation, they fit him pre-eminently for reflection and concentration. But there is more to them than this. They only do such good to the soul and affect it so powerfully because, in order to succeed with them, the soul has had to come to terms and agree with the body and the limbs. A yogi in the Perfect or Lotus posture is one of the finest existing symbols of man in complete possession of himself, of man who is "one" in his "three."

I shall not repeat here the description already given of silent meditation; I shall only give some pieces of advice and some warnings that it would be well to heed.

The ideal is to devote to meditation alone one of the two daily sessions of exercises recommended above. The morning session is certainly the more suitable. The Pole, the Full Backwards Bend, and the Folded Leaf together make up the first step in preparation. During these postures, your breath must become so gentle and steady that your pulse is felt but faintly; mine becomes imperceptible. A series of *prāṇāyāmas*, six or seven, will have the effect of spreading a suitable sense of calm through you. Then you take up the Perfect posture, or the Hero posture.

Calm: do not seek anything else. Do not be on the watch for extraordinary sensations, nor for psychological or parapsychological phenomena. In my opinion this would no longer be Christian Yoga; nor would it be Christianity, but some form of esotericism. Leave this kind of inquisitiveness to others, and set your mind firmly against running any risks. Like any other human technique, Yoga may be used or misused. Wine taken in moderation rejoices the heart of man.

Once this measure is exceeded, the most excellent and restorative drink works towards dissolution, degradation and death. Similarly with Yoga and with the various exercises intended to produce in man a condition favouring the total projection of his being towards God, and to create in him a special silence and void for the Lord to come and fill.

Everyone is acquainted with the performances of certain Indian yogis and with the surprising results reached by some Western adepts, such as levitation, thought-reading, trance and the suspension of vital powers. These are natural phenomena, although science is still puzzled about some of them. They have nothing in common with certain phenomena recorded in Christian mysticism, such as the passive purifications spoken of by St John of the Cross or St Teresa. It should, moreover, be noted that such phenomena receive scarcely any attention from the true yogis, whose sole preoccupation is to become one with the Absolute. We would call these phenomena "accidents"; the Christian has everything to gain by avoiding them.

In practice, do not give more than twelve to fifteen minutes to the preparatory exercises for meditation—postures, steadying the breath, and so on. Meditation itself, with the phases as described (pp. 126–33) (it may of course be greatly simplified) will not take longer than ten minutes to a quarter of an hour. That is a lot for a beginner, and quite enough for those who have come farther.

Do not exert yourself unduly to focus your gaze "on the root of the nose", as this point is sometimes described, or on any other fixed point on the body. Just look straight ahead. Rest your eyes on *one* object, or even on nothing at all. Seated facing a white wall on which there hangs a large crucifix, I have the impression that my eyes are focused in mid-air somewhere between the wall and me. What matters is that your gaze should be motionless and neutral. This is the reason for the advice that has been given: to choose a spot, always the same one, where one is liable to be disturbed as little as possible; a room set away on its own; a suitable corner or spot in that room; a portrait or landscape perhaps hung on the wall, but there should be nothing whose nature is likely to distract you or to scatter your thinking. Always sit on the same carpet and in the same garb. You must feel thoroughly at ease. You must not feel cold, and may therefore throw something over you in winter; but the window remains open, or ajar. Your garments should be sufficiently ample to cause no discomfort. Whatever squeezes or nips, such as a belt or underpants, must be discarded. Your surroundings have an important part to play; they have to be created, and you must take care not to introduce any disturbing factor that might screen you from God.

Once you are properly placed, let your gaze rest and do not move. You will *perhaps* observe a phenomenon of the following kind—I feel it is as well to let you know about it beforehand. At the same time as your gaze is gradually finding a neutral point, you may feel something inside you moving towards, and then stopping at, either the top of the cranium, or a point a little lower, or at chest level, or on a level with the heart. This phenomenon is produced by the nature or character of your meditation, according to whether it is primarily intellectual, emotive or affective. The Indian yogis, at the cost of efforts that are not without danger for our nervous temperaments, themselves pick out on the advice of their *guru* the "place" in the physical or pranic body where they will envisage the object of their meditation to be. One of the techniques of hesychastic prayer used to consist of looking for and discovering the "place of the heart". With regard to this, you may refer back to what I have already said about the prayer of the heart. But I must ask you to be cautious about all this. Accept any phenomenon that may occur. Do not try to produce one. Your prayer is not a game; I have already said this, and I remind you of it. Your quest is for God, or for the calm, silence and peace of heart in which you can, after a certain manner, converse with him. The remainder is scarcely of any interest to you, and will interest you not at all when you feel at your ease with silent prayer. These ten minutes will give you a fullness (it matters little whether you feel this or not); or more precisely they will replenish you, charge you up again. On the spiritual plane you will feel their effects for the whole of your day. On the intellectual level, a peculiar thing, a completely new phenomenon, will occur; the recollectedness of the morning will expand in you, I think, as it does in me, into greater activity. Your work will be easier; and the effort required practically nil. As for the physical effects, I refer you to what I pointed out above (p. 104) and what experience has proved over and over again. . . .

Here are a few concluding remarks.

1. Superiors of convents and novice-mistresses have asked me whether the method recommended in *La Voie du Silence* is suitable for women. Why not? Women, who are generally more supple than men, will have less difficulty in carrying out the postures; earlier in this book I have pointed out the only difference, which concerns breathing. At all events I know of several convents and monasteries where the method is being successfully practised. Naturally, it is not followed by everyone there, and should never be laid down as a rule binding on all. To those who question me on this matter, my reply is that they should read my book; there they will find the answer to their question.

2. Yoga exercises stimulate the activity of the glands, including the genital glands. The adept may therefore notice at certain times that his virility expresses itself more intensely

in more frequent and more copious emissions at night, for example. There is no need for him to worry about this. These slight inconveniences may, moreover, be avoided by practising certain postures, particularly the Pole and the Candle, which, as has already been pointed out, relieve congestion in the parts in question. All in all, I do not think that it belongs to the nature of Yoga to arouse the appetites of the flesh. If I am to believe my own experience and that of Indian yogis and of many Western adepts, it is much rather the opposite effect that is produced. Again—and this has also been verified empirically—although Yoga may excite the senses, it also strengthens the soul against "temptations".

3. Very nervous or highly-strung people are advised not to take up Yoga. For many of them the carrying out of the postures, which is normally very soothing, merely increases the tension and tires them out. In order to succeed, such people would have to clear right out of their minds every wish to succeed and especially any desire to enjoy the ripe fruits of Yoga at too early a season.

4. On similar grounds, one should abstain from Yoga when one is excessively tired.

5. Heart cases require much more careful handling. I know of several whose condition has been considerably improved by Yoga, and from whom certain kinds of distress have almost completely disappeared. But these persons went about things wisely. What is forbidden in heart cases is holding the breath. But proper breathing, and exercises that do not call for special effort or keen attention may have good results.

6. A final word for those keen on sport. Young people like to keep their muscles in condition. They may very well combine their normal physical culture with the exercises of Yoga. Alternatively they may set aside one of the two daily sessions for this training; or the two types of exercise may even be combined.

BY WAY OF CONCLUSION

ADDRESS WRITTEN BY REV. FR. RÉGAMEY, O.P.,
FOR THE FIRST EDITION.[1]

ON repeated occasions we have felt the lack of a competent handbook where Christians could find set out a comprehensive discipline of living, including the bodily aspect, which could promote spiritual balance and development. A Benedictine monk, using Yoga as a basis, has been working on and trying out such a method of discipline, and in this little book he gives an account of it.

A work of this kind may—or even should—give rise to misgivings on the part of anyone aware of the truth about Yoga and of certain attitudes that have been taken in the West towards it. But reading the book will allay these suspicions.

To begin with, there is a very definite risk of infatuation with the Asiatic doctrines and practice which so many of our contemporaries substitute for the Christian truths, or which they assimilate to Christian truths in a gross or subtle manner, thereby contaminating them. The author warns us against this danger, showing how inadmissible the philosophical and theological tenets to which Yoga has been married in India are for a Christian. There can be no hedging or equivocation about this. The elementary disciplines set out here have been "removed from their matrix", and it can be seen how they may be "introduced into a Christian climate", to a Christianity that is perfectly whole and integrated. This very fact will make it inexcusable for Christians who look for disciplines of this kind outside Christianity, on the grounds that

[1] See *Vie spirituelle*, Nov. 1956, pp. 429–42. I am most grateful to Fr. Régamey for kindly giving me permission to include this address here.

they are not to be found within it, to lay themselves open to aberrations. From now on they will easily be able to make good use of these disciplines in the Church itself, and in the spirit of the Church.

The root error is to ask any method to give more than it can. This is the mistake made by all asceticism, as Abbé Bremond has said, and is made in its most extreme form by unwise devotees of Yoga. Whether formally or implicitly, they consider themselves to be emanations of God, so that asceticism for them is a collection of methods by the use of which they claim to release that part of the "divine" they believe to be in them, and to make it firm and stable. They turn in on themselves. In contrast with ecstasy, coming out of oneself, the word "enstasy" has appropriately been applied to the frightening success of their procedures—when in fact they do "succeed". The author of this book very properly insists on the quality of "dialogue" inherent in true spiritual life, where the primacy is restored to pure *grace* and, for our part, to *charity*. For from making himself divine, the Christian forgets himself in the Other and in others. The disciplines are only intended to predispose, to remove certain barriers to the action of the supernatural. Viewed in this way they are not given any more prominence than they warrant.

Conversely, the risk also exists of underrating their usefulness, and of seeing in them nothing more than a form of sport or a hygienic practice. It may be said: "It has always been recognized that physical culture promotes intellectual and spiritual development; is this monk presenting us with anything more than a new system of gymnastics?" In fact he is offering something quite different. Sport is aimed at outer action, but the West possesses no method for making the body a fit instrument for contemplative life. We scarcely know any longer how to unite body, *animus* and *spiritus* in whole, indivisible acts. It is fashionable nowadays to rail at

Descartes, yet the affirmation that a human being is a composite whole remains too theoretical. Actual behaviour contradicts it. Only rarely does the behaviour of the body have the quality with which the spirit should endow it—for instance, in the act of worshipping. In the much vaunted "*mystique d'incarnation*", a system designed to "spiritualize" the body, the latter is exalted at the expense of the spirit rather than associated with the life of the spirit in its union with God. Liturgical and monastic customs should by their very nature act as a kind of "Yoga", but the awareness of this has been largely lost. One day I hope to point out how serious are the factors attacking it, and how profoundly modern mentality and the tenor of life today inhibit contemplation and disintegrate the composite wholeness of man. Instead of putting this mentality right, liturgical and even monastic practices are carried out in keeping with it. It is surely not without meaning that the need for a more thorough discipline should have been felt by a monk. It gives fresh significance to the elements of his life, which would certainly have contained enough for him if all kinds of present-day influences did not clash with it. Neither gymnastics in the strict sense nor spiritual considerations are able to effect this.

Finally, those who knew a great deal about Indian forms of Yoga may be turned against *La Voie du Silence*, as if this work claimed to solve the problem that engrosses them, that of a Yoga taken as far as possible and yet remaining Christian. Robert Amadou[2] rightly maintains that this little work does not broach the basic question, but leaves it unanswered. The aim of the author of this book is in fact very modest.

Any work should be judged in terms of what it sets out to do, and at the level at which it is intended. This work does not set out to solve the problems of Yoga in their full scope

[2] See *Combat*, 13 Sept. 1956.

and depth; in the warning words of an expert, "the problems that begin with the cessation of explicit thinking, a dark tunnel at the end of which no one knows what he will find". True, the problems of "Yoga the devourer" remain untouched. But Christians will benefit greatly from *La Voie du Silence* by integrating into their lives this modest discipline, which has already been tested out. I already know young monks who can bear witness to this.

The discipline itself consists of a short series of only fourteen exercises that M. Amadou amusingly but justly calls "yogoid". The fact must be insisted on that they present no danger if the author's instructions are properly carried out. Although they are quite elementary, they assume a degree of suppleness that will be unattainable by many elderly people. On the other hand, I cannot recommend too strongly anyone having spiritual charge of young people—I am thinking especially of superiors at seminaries and novice-masters—to take what this monk has to offer into very serious consideration. They should take care to situate the exercises properly, bearing in mind the possible errors of interpretation mentioned above, and against which the author has, moreover, warned us. The exercises in this book intentionally fall well short of techniques that would cause radical changes in the mind and psyche; but they work successfully to remedy a host of faults, against which one is normally powerless today. Children, teenagers, youths and young men who take up training on these lines will have no more general health problems and will feel their capacity for work increasing, their character becoming gentler and stronger, the need for sleep growing less; chastity will come more easily to them, and their life of prayer will have greater clarity, control and joyousness.

The author finds no difficulty in fitting his practices into the totality of Christian living. His life is nourished by the

Western tradition whose foremost representative is William of Saint-Thierry. He teaches these exercises only as one aspect of the whole life of man, who is, indissolubly, *anima, animus* and *spiritus,* and who above all is a child of God, anxious to show the greatest possible submissiveness to grace in all spheres.

It is not often that those who have taken the way of the spirit have had such a service done for them, a service of such effectivity and bearing so far—yet always provided that it is understood as the author intends. I am thinking with warmth of the many lives which, thanks to him, from now on can be led with greater *engagement.*

Paris.   FATHER P.-R. RÉGAMEY, O.P.

P.S. A recent testimony in support of *La Voie du Silence* has just reached me. It is taken from *The Reunion Record,* Tiruvalla Diocese, Kerala, India, No. 1, Christmas 1956: "The students at our seminary have taken up Yoga exercises as practised by Hindu sannyāsis (rishis). The conference report of the Indian episcopate (Seminary Section) writes of us as follows: 'At Tiruvalla the students, on getting up, give fifteen minutes to Yoga exercises as practised by sannyāsis. It has been found that this practice greatly improved the students' health. Common ailments amongst them are unknown; and alert, keen minds have been produced.'"

A NOTE ON THE PRAYER OF THE HEART

BY JEAN GOUILLARD

".... this very ancient practice ..."[1]—this reference made by Dr Déchanet will remind not a few readers of *The Way of a Pilgrim*,[2] revealed to the West about 1925, after a delay of seventy or eighty years. In it a pilgrim in search of salvation discovers with astonishment the secret of uninterrupted prayer at the school of a starets and from the *Philokalia*.[3] His confessions have a touchingly naïve fervour, and yet are not without a flavouring of esotericism.

There is no point in shutting our eyes to the fact that these confessions are presented in a certain order so as to defend a monastic movement exemplified by the startsi and nourished by the *Philokalia*. From this work the writer borrows the greater part of the vocabulary he uses in order to give an

---

[1] See above p 126.

[2] *The Way of a Pilgrim*, translated by R. M. French, 1930. S.P.C.K., 1941.

[3] The passages from the *Philokalia* quoted here may for the most part be found in *Writings from the Philokalia on Prayer of the Heart*, translated by E. Kadloubovsky and G. E. H. Palmer, Faber and Faber, London, 1951. All are contained in my *Petite Philocalie de la prière du cœur*, Paris, 1953.

(The *Philokalia* is a collection of writings by Fathers of the Eastern Church from the fourth century to the fourteenth, and exists in three versions: Greek, Slavonic, and Russian. When the title *Philokalia* is used in this appendix, the Russian version is intended. It is from this version that the French and English translations have been made. Wherever possible, the English translation by Kadloubovsky and Palmer mentioned above in the author's footnote has been used here, and acknowledged under the abbreviated title *Writings from the Philokalia*; in one or two cases, another set of texts put into English by the same translators has been quoted from: *Early Fathers from the Philokalia*, Faber and Faber, London, 1954.—TRANSLATOR.)

account of his mystical experiences. A lot more would be needed to make one suspect the authenticity of experiences of this sort, and to assume even that the pilgrim himself was merely a didactic fiction; but we are given too much in these confessions for us to be able to allow them indiscriminately an authority of their own, unsupported by the famous book.

This book, the *Philokalia*, which, together with the Bible and a store of bread, forms the entire worldly goods of the pilgrim, is in fact a library in itself, for it collates the majority, or all the better known, of the Greek masters of the contemplative life from the fourth to the fifteenth century. It enjoyed a tremendous reputation in Russia during last century. For the pilgrim and his fellows, who must have been legion, the *Philokalia* was the one and only storehouse of the secrets of prayer, or rather of a form of prayer that can with certainty be traced back to about A.D. 1250, and that has marked the whole development of Graeco-Russian spirituality from then on.

To one of the most traditional kinds of contemplative prayer—the "prayer of Jesus"—it links a technique of mental concentration which suggests, and even calls for, a comparison with that of Yoga.

Its descriptions are always too fragmentary and full of allusions to constitute a guide-book in their own right. Whether overtly or not, they consistently disregard the considerable part played by the spiritual director. Their intention is much rather to whet the keenness of the neophyte and to recommend a set of practices to him, than to put a tool in his hands. In this respect, both the passages of *Philokalia* and the personal revelations of the Russian pilgrim are equally deceptive. Once these allowances have been made, it is possible to form some idea of the matter.

The sources available to us distinguish three forms of concentration, of which the main is breath-control. It is both the shortest and the most thorough, as well as being the most trying. Although success is almost inevitable, it does not come at the first attempt. This form of concentration at first discouraged the Russian pilgrim, who had to fall back on simpler means.

Breath-control (which, it must be emphasized, is inseparable from prayer) demands a twofold preparation, moral and physical.

The first of these preparations is described by Pseudo-Simeon in the thirteenth century in the following terms: "Before setting yourself to the task, you must be in possession of three predisposing conditions: you must be withdrawn from all thoughts, whether lawful or forbidden; your conscience must be free from reproach; you must be completely detached from any impression that would incline you towards the century or even towards your body."

On the subject of physical discipline the authors are vaguer. They agree on the need for a cell that is quiet and closed; some also wish it dark (Callistus and Ignatius in the fourteenth century). Several recommend a low seat with no back—a stool—and Gregory of Sinai (†1346) goes so far as to specify that it should be ten inches high (half a cubit).

The psycho-physical phase is sometimes expounded, particularly by the early theoreticians, with the use of a fairly materialistic imagery, which has played into the hands of its fourteenth-century opponents, such as Barlaam of Calabria. This use of language is due both to the inability of these writers to free themselves from an antiquated science of man and also to their wish to give a scientific interpretation of phenomena, whose good effects they were able to perceive with greater exactness than that with which they were able to penetrate to their true nature. This rubbish must be thrown aside in order to go straight to the aim that inspires it all—to restore to the spirit that fullness that is by nature liable to

flow away and, as it were, to dissipate itself in futile thinking at
the expense of the one thing necessary, the "remembrance of
God". This process depends mainly on disciplined breathing.

The exercise itself has two aspects: a controlled slowing up
of the rhythm of breathing, and an exploration of the visceral
self. The first of these is always mentioned, the second is
frequently passed over in silence.

Here are the two most ancient references, which may in
fact have come from the one hand.

> And so, having collected your mind within you, lead it
> into the channel of breathing through which air reaches
> the heart and, together with this inhaled air, force your
> mind to descend into the heart and to remain there.
> Accustom it, brother, not to come out of the heart too
> soon, for at first it feels very lonely in that inner seclusion
> and imprisonment. But when it gets accustomed to it, it
> begins on the contrary to dislike its aimless circling out-
> side, for it is no longer unpleasant and wearisome for it
> to be within.[4]

> Place your chin against your chest, turn the eye of your
> body, likewise that of your mind, to the middle of your
> stomach, that is to say, to your navel. Restrict your inhala-
> tions through the nose in such a way as not to be breathing
> freely and, with your mind, explore your visceral organs
> in search of the place of the heart, where all the powers
> of the soul are pleased to frequent.[5]

The fact that many writers leave out the exploration of the
body is probably because it was guarded as a mystery. The
Russian pilgrim, in other respects very discreet about factual
details of technique, is thoroughly aware that one has to reach
the stage of "opening the threshold of the heart"[6]; and the

---

[4] Nicephorus the Solitary (c. A.D. 1250), "Profitable Discourse on Sobriety",
Writings from the Philokalia, p. 33.

[5] Pseudo-Simeon in the same period.   [6] *The Way of a Pilgrim.*

blind man whom he himself initiated later on, experienced light-filled phenomena in his heart which are not unknown in the exploration already mentioned.[7] Moreover, the references available from both ends of the tradition are sufficiently explicit to remove any doubts on the matter.

If there is any point generally agreed on by all sources, it is that the control of breathing is not an end. It is only the condition that most favours the practice of monologic prayer, "Lord Jesus Christ, Son of God, have mercy on me". It will be seen that the invocation may discard the breathing technique, while the latter loses all point if divorced from the former.

Once recollectedness has been achieved, monology, whether spoken or purely mental, makes use of this condition to aim at linking all human powers into a single activity that brings them all into operation according to the function for which they are designed. "Do not have any other occupation or meditation than the cry 'Lord Jesus Christ, have mercy on me'", advises Nicephorus, the earliest teacher of this method. With greater explicitness, Theoleptus of Philadelphia (†c. A.D. 1325) tells us: "Intellect runs over the words of the supplication, while the spirit remains turned wholly to God. The intellect ceaselessly suggests the name of God, the spirit is intensely attentive to the invocation of the Holy Name, and the light of the divine gnosis spreads its shadow over the soul."

The prayer of Jesus (to use the name given to it throughout the tradition) in fact ideally expresses the basic bi-polarity of God-me, at the time as it contains the whole essence of Salvation. "The words 'Lord Jesus Christ' direct the spirit towards him whom they name; the words 'have mercy on me' bring him back to himself as if it were impossible for him to stand the idea of not praying for himself."[8] Seven or

[7] *Op. cit.*
[8] Callistus and Ignatius, in the fourteenth century.

eight centuries before, Hesychius of Jerusalem had already put this more concisely, "To each breath you take, join the name of Jesus and humility".

The invocation itself is linked to disciplined breathing and fitted to it, with variants that do not invalidate the principle. The blind man in the *Way*[9] says or thinks half the invocation as he breathes in, and the other half as he breathes out. Gregory of Sinai used to recommend one to switch one's attention from the first half to the second from time to time, though not too often. Callistus and Ignatius are of the opinion that those who have gone far in these practices may limit their attention only to the name of Jesus.

Once all these conditions have been observed, the "prayer of Jesus" becomes in the true sense "the prayer in or of the heart".

Before dealing with its effects, it is appropriate to discuss two fairly simple variants familiar to the readers of the *Way*, which lead towards the full form and to some extent share its properties.

The first variant consists of uttering as long a chain of invocations to Jesus as possible. In doing this our Russian pilgrim utters three thousand a day, then six and finally twelve thousand. He thus reaches a kind of irresistible invocation which from now on acts in advance of his own initiative; his lips keep moving in sleep and have already pronounced the prayer even before he has had time to think of it on waking. Without realizing it, he is having an experience which the "early Fathers", as Cassian called them, used to hand down to their followers as a secret, and to bring about which they frequently used the *Deus in adjutorium*. What happens to him had already happened to one of the Fathers he respected most, St Simeon the New Theologian († A.D. 1022): "As yet uninitiated in these secrets, he was shouting

[9] *The Way of a Pilgrim.*

aloud in amazement tirelessly 'Lord, have mercy on me' (as he discovered once he came back to himself); for until then he was completely unaware that his mouth had been speaking and that his voice had been heard by witnesses."

One day, the pilgrim is astounded to discover that the prayer of Jesus has taken up the rhythm of the beating of his heart. "I felt that the prayer was of its own accord entering my heart; I mean that my heart, beating regularly, was setting itself in some way to recite, by its own action, the holy words on each beat, for instance 1—Lord, 2—Jesus, 3—Christ, and so on."[10] The treatises in the *Philokalia* do not stress this method, which, notwithstanding its extraordinary results, do not dispense with what we choose to call the royal way, that of breath-control; and this is adequately shown by the behaviour of the Russian pilgrim in teaching the various forms one after the other to his blind pupil.

The theoreticians and adepts of the method endow it with a wealth of extraordinary effects, all of which are marked with a character easily perceptible to the senses—euphoria, a feeling of universal benevolence towards all creatures, indifference to physical suffering, tears, effusions of light, fleeting communications with a deceased spiritual director, perception of the Kingdom of Heaven within oneself. The Russian pilgrim declares that he has experienced all this, and it is a fact that what he read promised him no less.

This collection of effects which has been put together from the *Way* could also be made from the *Philokalia*. It provides incontrovertible evidence of dangerous confusions and simplifications. The necessary distinction has not been made between natural benefits resulting from postures and exercises that are essentially physical and the graces which may be received during or after a particularly exalted prayer. The account of this method is given as though it were something

10 *Op. cit.*

complete in itself, and yet it is given in an abridged form; and when this is joined to the exaggerated value accorded to its results, it is small wonder that the person practising this discipline is led to attribute the effects of psycho-physical training to a prayer that is already fairly widely regarded as miraculous.

From a different source, which in all other respects supports the method, we can learn of further cases where people have become victims of this very misapprehension. Neophytes who, we are told, were badly prepared and not equipped with the necessary discretion and obedience severely compromised their health and developed chest complaints. Yet others, carried away by the mirage promised them, were brought by their practice of internal exploration and their search for the place of the heart to impure illuminations and above all to satisfactions of a kind that no longer had anything in common with the euphoria of contemplation.

True, this is not the case with our Russian pilgrim. But if he had been better informed about the nature of the method of breathing, he would have been less troubled by his sense of duty to the Indian yogis. "The monks of India and Bokhara have borrowed from them [from the holy Fathers of the *Philokalia*!] the technique of the prayer of the heart, but my staretz told me that they have disfigured and spoilt it."[11]

On this point the pilgrim bases himself directly on the codifiers of the method. After them more moderate voices had been raised, but these do not appear to have reached him. Gregory Palamas († A.D. 1359), who, though harassed by adversaries, nevertheless kept an enlightened mind, had thoroughly understood the natural, provisional character of the technique, as the following lines show.

[11] *Op. cit.*

It is not out of place to invite someone, especially a beginner, to look at himself and to introduce his intellect into his body together with his breath. . . . Being a novice still, he does not realize that nothing in the world acts more strongly against self-consideration or is better able to restore him. For this reason some writers advise him to control the breathing by pausing for a short while so as to retain the spirit at the same time as he holds his breath. This should be continued until, with the grace of God, he has reached the stage of having purified his intellect and barred it off from the external world, and is able to gather up wholly in a unifying act of concentration. Everyone can verify that attending to something with the intellect spontaneously results in a slowing down of the breathing rhythm; this happens during any act of intense reflection, and particularly with those persons who cultivate silence of mind and body.

Gregory is echoed by his contemporaries Callistus and Ignatius, writing presumably under the same influence:

You must understand, brother, that methods, rules and exercises owe their existence solely to our inability to pray in our hearts purely and without experiencing distraction. When by grace of Jesus Christ we have acquired this ability, we discard plurality and unite ourselves directly and ineffably with the One, the Undifferentiated, he who unifies . . . but this is a privilege most rare.

There is scarcely any echo of these reservations in the method proposed by the pilgrim or by his starets, who does however happen to distinguish between the assistance given by the natural habit and the freedom and ease conferred by grace.

The ambiguity in the general attitude to this point makes it impossible to work out how effective and useful the contribution made by the method has been over the long period during which the way of silence has been held in honour. But the very existence of the method is in itself an important fact; and it is appropriate to throw some light on its origins, as far as this may be done.

The pilgrim has no doubt that the prayer of the hesychasts comes immediately out of the Gospel. "In the *Philokalia* all teachings on inner prayer are drawn from divine writ, from the holy Bible."[12] Granted, the *Philokalia* is admirably suited to confirm him in this opinion. Apart from the technical instructions on breath-control and the search of the place of the heart, hesychast writing after the twelfth century simply makes use of a collections of ideas and expressions sanctified by a steady stream of teachers including St Simeon Metaphrastes, Bishop Diadochus and the whole Sinai school with John of the Ladder, Hesychius of Jerusalem, and Philotheus. Unfortunately, the aphoristic style adopted by the majority, coupled with the hyperbole natural to them all, leaves us without objective descriptions of processes or states.

Several points nevertheless seem to be established. Firstly, already at a very early period of the history of monachism, the invocation of Jesus has come to occupy a privileged position in the prayer and meditation of ascetics. It exorcizes devils and thoughts, it plunges one back into the "remembrance of God" which is always liable to vanish, and it possesses extraordinary properties. Secondly, the adepts of this method have the ambition of making this prayer automatic and, they readily think, spontaneous, by tireless repetition. In the words of Macarius the Copt, who faithfully sums up this psychology, whatever his true identity may be, "let your heart at all times send up to heaven this ever gentle fountain—Our Lord Jesus Christ". Thirdly, the invocation of Jesus is very quickly assimilated to breathing, and is as vital and necessary

[12] *Op. cit.*

as breathing. At some period difficult to ascertain, but which cannot be any later than the eighth century, the association of the invocation with breathing was undertaken. Hesychius of Jerusalem makes the following promise: "If you wish to live in peace and ease and keep your heart watchful without difficulty, let the prayer of Jesus cleave to your breath and you shall succeed before long."

A step had to be taken to get from the amount of attention that breathing had to be given for all this, to full breath-control in the proper sense of the word; just as a step also had to be made from the physical treatment of the heart, given in detail by St Simeon Metaphrastes and Bishop Diadochus, in order to reach the mental exploration in the method of Nicephorus the Solitary. At what point of history the step was taken remains the obscure part of the problem and for the time being it is insoluble.

It is justifiable to assume Eastern influences, which may or may not have been transmitted by Islam, where these methods have also been practised, sometimes with remarkable subtlety. There should be nothing shameful in borrowing in this way. Methods of mental concentration have the worth and justification of their usage. They are fine servants, like the body, and nothing more; yet this is already a great deal.

EXTRACTS FROM THE *PHILOKALIA*

THE gaps left in the account and the confusion in the plans
—partly attributable to an awkwardness of style rather
than to disorderly thinking—may interfere with the historical
and psychological evaluation, as well as with practical ex-
perimentation of the methods of concentration mentioned
above. The *Philokalia* remains a monument raised to silence,
if the untranslatable word *hesychia* may be put in this way—
this active repose of the powers, the ideal (theoretical) centre
of which is solitude. Several extracts may be able to touch
on this aspect and make up for the negative effect of this
account.

The *Philokalia* is a book for monks, in the fundamental
sense of hermit or anchorite. It harks back to the desert
origins of monasticism. In the desert, only the hands can find
any interest in work, which is a means of subsisting rather
than a form of penitence and does not express the desire for
development and growth. It leaves the soul of the man himself completely at the disposal of the "inner task", namely,
to maintain as unbroken as possible an awareness of the only
Presence, God. This simplification, taken to extremes, of
the situation of man (of which perhaps stylitism, living poised
in empty space, is a more striking expression than living in the
desert) does not avoid a schematization of spirituality, and
may be linked with certain superstitious axioms about life.
From this arises a tendency to tiresome repetition, of little
training value, cluttered up with metaphors and pedantic

reminiscings. This is foreign to the first generations of monks in the desert, but has not spared their successors, nor the *Philokalia*, which is their interpreter. This factor must be taken into account; the only thing to be held firm is a keen awareness of the fundamental laws of union with God in silence.

To unite with God in prayer is to restore the state of Paradise; the union is based on purifying and setting at peace the human faculties. Purification starts from outside and works gradually inwards. To begin with, it consists of following the commandments and reforming one's conduct. Then comes the shutting out of "thoughts", of the thinking with images that veils the vision of the intellect, whether this thinking has become infected with attachment to forbidden things, or to things which in themselves are legitimate. After that there follows the monological prayer which works towards purification and at the same time feeds the faculties purified. The final stage is contemplation. These are the principal common themes of the *Philokalia*.

REDISCOVERING THE "REMEMBRANCE OF GOD"

"At the source of every evil you will find distraction" (Poemen, 43).

"Sight, taste, and indeed all the senses dissipate the memory of the heart as soon as they are allowed to exceed proper limits; of this Eve gives us the first proof. As long as she did not look with favour on the forbidden tree, she faithfully remembered the commandment. . . . No sooner had she thought of the fruit with pleasure, no sooner had she touched and finally tasted it with keen delight, than she felt drawn by the joys of the senses. . . . From then on it is difficult for the intellect to keep God and his commandments in mind. Let us therefore cross this existence, so favourable to deceit, like blind men, with our gaze fixed on the innermost place of our hearts in a flawless remembrance of God" (Bishop Diadochus, 56).

"It is ordained that man must put before all things the universal commandment—to remember God—of which it is said: 'thou shalt remember the Lord thy God' (Deut. 8.18). For, by the reverse of that which destroys us, we may be secure. What destroys us is forgetfulness of God, which shrouds the commandments in darkness and despoils us of all good" (Gregory of Sinai, 17, from *Writings from the Philokalia*, p. 40).

"The origin and cause of thoughts lies in the splitting up, by man's transgression, of his single and simple memory, which has thus lost the memory of God and, becoming multiple instead of simple, and varied instead of single, has fallen a prey to its own forces.

"To cure this original memory of the deceitful and harmful memory of thoughts means to bring it back to its ancient simplicity. . . . Memory can be cured by a constant remembrance of God, consolidated by the action of prayer" (Gregory of Sinai, 60, 61, from *Writings from the Philokalia*, p. 48).

"Keep God in your minds that he shall not cease to be mindful of you. Being mindful of you he will save you and give you a share in all his wealth. Do not forget him in empty distractions, if you do not wish him to forget you in his turn, at a time of temptation. When you are in a condition of euphoria, dwell near him in your heart; for in this way he will replenish your store of steadfastness to lay up provision against future difficulties. Keep yourself unceasingly in his presence, thinking of him, remembering him in your heart.

Otherwise, if you see him only at a distance, you may lack confidence and show yourself timid with him. Diligence in keeping turned to God makes for a profound sense of confidence" (St Isaac of Nineveh, V).

PURIFYING THE FACULTIES

(Purifying the faculties is primarily a task of attentiveness, watchfulness, *nepsis*—a state of particularly active vigilance.)

"Do you wish for prayer? Renounce everything, and you will obtain everything" (Abba Evagrius, *Of Prayer*, 36).

"He who renounces worldly things, such as women and wealth and so on, makes the outer man a monk, but not yet the inner man. But he who renounces the passionate thought of these things, makes a monk of the inner man as well, that is, the mind. Such a man is a true monk" (Hesychius of Jerusalem, 70, from *Writings from the Philokalia*, pp. 293–4).

"Let us strive to bring to Christ's judgement seat more than a man who is a monk—let us strive to bring a truly monastic mind" (Abba Evagrius).

"As far as you can, when you pray, make a deaf-mute of your intellect; in this way you will be fit for prayer" (Abba Evagrius, *Of Prayer*, 11).

"When we have acquired a certain skill in abstinence and withdrawal from visible evils produced by the five senses, we shall be able also to guard our heart with Jesus, to have it illumined by him and with a warm disposition to savour his blessings in our mind. For the only reason why we were given the law of purifying the heart is to have clouds of evil thoughts driven away from the atmosphere of the heart, and dispersed by constant attention, so that we can see clearly, as on a bright fine day, the Sun of truth—Jesus, and can be in some measure illumined in our mind by the words of his glory" (Philotheus of Sinai, 8, from *Writings from the Philokalia*, p. 326).

"And so every hour and every moment let us zealously guard our heart from thoughts obscuring the mirror of the soul, which should contain, drawn and imprinted on it, only the radiant image of Jesus Christ, . . ." (Philotheus of Sinai, 23, from *Writings from the Philokalia*, p. 333).

"There can be no pacifying the intellect without also pacifying the body. The partition between them cannot be broken down without silence and prayer" (Mark the Anchorite, *Century II*, 29).

"A hesychast is he who being without body strives to retain his soul within the bounds of its bodily home" (St John of the Ladder, 27, from *Writings from the Philokalia*, p. 28).

"Silence of the body is obtained by understanding and control of external behaviour and the activity of the senses. Silence of the soul is achieved by knowing thoughts for what they are while remaining in inviolate possession of one's intellect" (St John of the Ladder, 27).

"A small hair worries the eye and a small care destroys silence, for silence means laying aside of all thoughts not bearing on the work of salvation, and renunciation of all cares, even for matters of good report" (St John of the Ladder, 27, from *Writings from the Philokalia*, p. 186).

"The first work of silence is freedom from cares for all things, whether of good or evil report, for he who opens the door to the former is sure to fall into the latter. The second work is prayer free from laziness; and the third —unrobbed doing of the heart" (St John of the Ladder, 27, from *Writings from the Philokalia*, pp. 186–7).

"Attention is unceasing silence of the heart, free of all thoughts. At all times, constantly and without ceasing, it breathes Christ Jesus, the Son of God and God, and him alone, it calls upon him, and with him fights bravely against the enemies, and makes confession to him who has power to forgive sins.

"Sobriety is the steadfast setting up of the thought of the mind and posting it at the door of the heart, so that it sees alien thoughts as they come, those thieves and robbers, and hears what these destroyers say and do; and sees what is the image inscribed and figured in them by the demons, who are trying thus to seduce the mind of fantasy" (Hesychius of Jerusalem, 5, 6, from *Writings from the Philokalia*, p. 280).

"One way of sobriety is to watch closely imagination or suggestion, for without imagination Satan cannot form thoughts and exhibit them to the mind to seduce it by deceit.

"And another is to keep the heart always deeply silent, all thought stilled, and to pray.

"Another is to call humbly and unceasingly on our Lord Jesus Christ for help.

"All these doings, beloved, keep off evil thoughts like door-keepers" (Hesychius of Jerusalem, 14–16, 18, from *Writings from the Philokalia*, p. 282).

"Be steadfast in attention of the mind, and you shall not be overburdened by temptations. Retreat from this, and suffer what befalls" (Hesychius of Jerusalem, 54, from *Writings from the Philokalia*, p. 291).

"Attention in search of prayer will find prayer, for if there is anything that attention does lead to, it is prayer. Hence the reason for developing and training it" (Abba Evagrius, *Of Prayer*, 149).

"The smoke of wood fire is painful to the eyes; but later when light appears it brings delight in place of discomfort. In the same way attention, constantly straining the eyes of the mind, is painful and tiring to the head. But Jesus, being invoked in prayer, when he comes brings light to the heart. Remembrance of him together with illumination (of our inner man) brings us the highest blessing of all (that is, the Lord himself)" (Philotheus of Sinai, 29, from *Writings from the Philokalia*, p. 336).

"If the heart is completely freed of fantasies, it begins to give birth to divine and mysterious thoughts, which play within it as fishes play and dolphins leap in a calm sea" (Hesychius of Jerusalem, 156, from *Writings from the Philokalia*, p. 311).

"So then, as I said, it is in the nature of these two things, sobriety and prayer to Jesus, to be in union one with the other. For sobriety is complete attention and constant prayer; and prayer in turn means the utmost sobriety and attention of mind" (Hesychius of Jerusalem, 94, from *Writings from the Philokalia*, p. 297).

MONOLOGY

(This is both an instrument of purification, and a source of sustenance in contemplation. It is spoken at the outset, but becomes gradually more and more interior. Though often identified with the "prayer of Jesus", it may make use of other expressions.)

"To curb irascibility, appropriate silence; to curb concupiscence, discipline in food and drink; to curb refractory reason, monologic prayer" (Elias Ekdikos, 169).

"In your prayer, shun grace-notes and flowery excesses; one word was enough to reconcile the thief and the prodigal son with God" (St John of the Ladder, 28).

"Do not polish the language you use in prayer. Often the mere babblings of a child touch his Father in heaven. Do not take pains to use a wealth of words, for in so doing you will waste your intellectual powers in the search. Prolixity in prayer results in the diffusion of the intellect amongst products of the imagination. Monology, on the other hand, is made to recollect the intellect. If the phrasing of your prayer arouses in you a feeling of attraction or compunction, dwell on it, for this means that your guardian angel has joined in your prayer" (St John of the Ladder, 28).

"The unceasing repetition of the name of God is a remedy that goes beyond destroying passion; it destroys the source of passion" (St Barsanuphius the Great, 421).

"The perfect artist in perfect prayer has said: 'I would rather speak five words which my mind utters. . . .' (I Cor. 14.19). This is beyond the grasp of children; and that is why, because of our imperfection, we pray using diversity and quantity" (St John of the Ladder, 28).

"When we block up the outlets of the intellect with

remembrance of God, it demands absolutely of us an activity that satisfies its own need of activity. To it we should give the 'Lord Jesus' as its whole programme. For it is written: '. . . . it is only through the Holy Spirit that anyone can say, Jesus is the Lord' (I Cor. 12.3). But let it contemplate without ceasing this pearl in its treasure so jealously that it shall never allow itself to fall a prey to any product of the imagination. All those who continuously repeat this holy and glorious name in the depths of the heart will finally reach a condition in which they can see the light of their minds" (Bishop Diadochus, 59).

"A man who thereupon wishes to cleanse his heart should constantly inflame it by memory of our Lord Jesus, having this (that is, memory of the Lord) as the sole object of his thoughts and his constant spiritual doing. For a man who wishes to rid himself of his rot should not now pray and now not pray, but must constantly exercise himself in prayer with sobriety, even if he lives far away from the houses of prayer. A man wishing to refine gold must not leave his furnace without fire for however short a time, lest the ore harden again. In the same way, a man who now remembers God, now not, loses by stopping prayer whatever he appears to have gained by its practice" (Bishop Diadochus, 97, from *Writings from the Philokalia*, pp. 230-31).

"If the soul is excited by anger, disturbed by intemperance, or distressed by a serious discouragement (all affections of the irascible, the concupiscible, and of reason), the spirit is unable even under compulsion to grasp the remembrance of Jesus. Darkened by the storm of passions, it loses command over its own sensitivity. Desire is now powerless to stamp the seal of meditation inviolably on its own recollection, which has coarsened and hardened under the passions. Is the soul, on the contrary, liberated from the passions? Should forgetfulness for a moment deprive the intellect of the object of its desire, it regains its own activity as rapidly as possible and fervidly seizes its beloved and salutary prey. For in this state the soul itself has the grace to meditate and to cry, with grace, 'Lord Jesus'. Likewise a mother teaches her child the word 'dada' by repeating it with him, until he has got into the way of calling for his father with confidence, even in sleep. Whence the words of the Apostle: 'Only as before, the Spirit comes to the aid of our weakness, when we do not know what prayer to offer, to pray as we ought, the Spirit himself intercedes for us, with groans beyond all utterance' (Rom. 8.26). As we are still children in respect of the state of perfect prayer, the aid of the Spirit is indispensable to us, so that, with all our thoughts contained and softened by its ineffable gentleness, we shall be able to come with whole hearts to the remembrance and love of God our Father. That is why it is in the Spirit that we cry when we are taught to cry out without ceasing to God the Father: 'Abba, Father'" (Rom. 8.15) (Bishop Diadochus, 61).

"To call on Jesus perpetually with warm desire, full of sweetness and joy, fills the air of the heart with joyous stillness; and this comes from extreme attention. But he who perfectly purifies the heart is Jesus Christ alone, the Son of God and God, the Cause and Maker of all good things" (Hesychius of Jerusalem, 91, from *Writings from the Philokalia*, p. 297).

PURE PRAYER

(The intellect restored to its pristine function)

"Prayer without distraction constitutes the supreme functioning of the intellect" (Abba Evagrius, *Of Prayer*, 34a).

"What is prayer? An intellect freed from all earthly bonds and a heart wholly turned to the expectations of hope. Otherwise, one does like the peasant who scatters different kinds of seeds in the same furrow, or harnesses an ox and a donkey to his cart" (St Isaac of Nineveh, 74).

"The thinking soul has a forecourt, namely sense; it has a temple, namely reason; and it has a priest, the intellect. An intellect pillaged by harmful thoughts is to be found in the forecourt; an intellect plundered by permitted thoughts is in the temple; an intellect that escapes both is judged fit to enter the sanctuary" (Elias Ekdikos, 148).

"Let prayer cleave as firmly to the intellect as the sun's rays do to the sun. Without prayer preoccupations of the senses shut away the intellect in their arid clouds and deprive it of its native resplendence" (Elias Ekdikos, 79).

"Devils are intensely averse to pure prayer. It is not the wide front of opposing forces that frightens them, in the way that the enemy frightens an army. What frightens them is the agreement and harmony of the three—intellect with reason, and reason with sense" (Elias Ekdikos, 175).

"Who is there in this generation who is wholly free from passionate thoughts, who has acquired the pure immaterial ceaseless prayer, which is the distinguishing feature of the inward man?" (Hesychius of Jerusalem, 71, from *Writings from the Philokalia*, p. 294).

"One does not have to learn to see, for this is nature's business. No more does one learn from anyone else the magnificent things in prayer. Prayer bears within itself its master, God, 'who taught man all that man knows' (Ps. 93.10), who gives prayer to him who prays, and blesses the years of the just" (St John of the Ladder, 28).

POSTURES OF PRAYER

(Apologia for the breathing technique)

"When there are no witnesses to our praying who might flatter our pride, we should make ourselves take up the outer attitude of prayer. With those who are imperfect, the intellect frequently imitates the attitude of the body" (St John of the Ladder, 28).

"Our soul is endowed with many powers, and it uses the body as an instrument, to which it gives life. What is the organ used as an instrument for its activity by that power which we call mind? No one ever thought that mind resided in nails or eyelashes, in nostrils or cheeks. But all agree that it is inside us—they disagree only as to which inner organ it uses as an instrument. For some place it in the brain as in some citadel; others say its seat is in the innermost part of the heart. We agree with the latter, adding only that it is not as in a vessel that our mental power is so confined in the heart, for it is incorporeal; nor is it outside it, as though something connected with the heart; but it is in the heart as in its organ. . . .

"Therefore, striving with diligent sobriety to keep watch over our mental power, to govern and correct it rightly, how can we succeed in this except by collecting the mind, which is dispersed outside by the senses, and introducing it within, into that very heart which is the storehouse of thoughts? Thus the blessed Macarius says a little after the words I have quoted, 'It is there we must look to see whether grace has inscribed the laws of the Spirit.' There—where?—In the chief organ, where stands the throne of grace, and where are the mind and all the thoughts of the soul, that is, in the heart.

"You see how essential it is for those, who have decided to keep attention in themselves in silence, to turn the mind back and confine it in the body, especially in that part, which is the innermost body within the body and which we call the heart?" (Gregory Palamas, *On the Blessed Hesychasts*, 3, 4, 5, from *Early Fathers from the Philokalia*, pp. 403–4.

"One of the great teachers says that since the fall the inner man usually accords with the outer (with outer movements and postures). If this be so, why not accept it that a man who strives to turn his mind within is greatly helped in this if, instead of letting his eyes wander hither and thither, he turns them inwards and fixes them in his breast? When the eyes wander outside, the mind becomes dispersed among things through seeing them. In the same way, if the eyes are turned inwards, this movement of theirs will naturally lead the mind too inside the heart in a man who strives to reverse the movement of his mind, that is, to recall it from outside and lead it inwards" (Gregory Palamas, *On the Blessed Hesychasts*, 11, from *Early Fathers from the Philokalia*, p. 406).